LIFE COACHING FOR ADULTS ON THE AUTISM SPECTRUM

Discovering Your True Potential

Jaclyn Hunt MA, ACAS, BCCS

ASD Life Coaches LLC

ISBN-13: 978-1-7371074-1-5
ISBN-13: 978-1-7371074-0-8

Cover design by: James V Carroll www.jvcarroll.com
Printed in the United States of America

For Joseph, my love.

CONTENTS

ACKNOWLEDGMENTS

There are many people I need to thank that made this work possible. First and foremost my husband Joseph who loved, encouraged and supported me in this journey. Without him, this book and my life's work would simply not exist. To my parents Maria and George who have always loved and encouraged me in everything that I choose to do. My brother Frank for reading through my book many times and giving me his expert advice on how to make this as thorough and complete as possible and to my sister-in-law Nichole for always being excited and supportive of my work in every way.

I also need to thank many of my colleagues for helping me to formulate my methods over the years, particularly Adrian Wensley and Sky Savittiere for their input, development and deep understanding of the levels of friendship. Without them, that model would not be in the form that you see here in this book today. It has evolved with their help and will continue to do so for many years to come. I value their professionalism and friendship most dearly.

I want to thank Matthew Hoel for his beautiful Foreword to kick off this book and for his tremendous progress and friendship over the years. Justin Osborn needs a mention for not only his growth and friendship but also his passion to abolish all of the autism stereotypes that currently exist in this world today. I also want to acknowledge Reese Gassmann who, like everyone I work with, has made me so proud. Additionally, I would like to thank all of my coaches. Particularly, Rosanne Mazzarelli, CCC for her friendship and tremendous ability to connect with her clients. I told you I was bringing you with me! Obviously, I need to thank Francesco Paladino, CCC who jumped on board, helped this company grow and has a work ethic that rivals my own and then some. Check out his touching Foreword in Part II of this book for the story of how this alliance came to be. Also, Gretchen McIntire, CCC has not only been a valuable part of my team, her growth personally and as a professional over the years has truly made a difference in what we are trying to accomplish as coaches for neurodiverse individuals.

Additionally, I am truly thankful to Lori Gassmann for providing a beautiful Foreword for the third part of this book. I believe her experience as a parent resonates with so many and adds to the completeness of this work. Then there is Jamie. I estimate that I have known him for approximately 20 years now and through the Muppet Fan Forums of yesteryear grew friendships and professionalism the likes of which the world may never see again. His gorgeous artwork graces the cover of my book and I am honored that his creation is the face of my work.

Lastly, I would like to thank each and every one of my clients. There are too many to mention individually but you all know who you are. Thank you for the opportunity to be apart of your lives and to do my very best to show you how to live up to your fullest potential.

INTRODUCTION

Why a Life Coach and
not a Therapist?

I realized at a young age that I had a gift — I could actually feel the emotions of others around me. At times, it was confusing and overwhelming, but as I matured and honed my skills, I was better able to separate my "stuff" from the rest of the world. To this very day, I can go sit on a bench in the park, the mall, or any public place, and within 15 minutes, someone will sit next to me and begin to tell me his or her life story. Naturally, as an empath, I became interested in people, and I began to study psychology at Rutgers University in New Brunswick, New Jersey, before going on to earn my Master's degree in the Behavioral Sciences with a specialization in Psychological Services at Kean University in Union, NJ. My goal was to become a Marriage and Family Therapist; however, something stood in my way. While I highly respect the field of psychology and believe in many of the methods psychologists and therapists around the world successfully utilize on a daily basis, I feel that there is a very large gap in terms of understanding Autism Spectrum Disorders, particularly in adulthood.

Through my life experiences, I have discovered and fine-tuned my own methods of understanding and communicating with ASD adults. I know how to bridge the gap in communication and actually make progress in people's daily lives because I have seen it and experienced it for myself. A therapist, even a highly qualified therapist, does not always have the deep personal understanding of how each moment in an ASD adult's life can be a struggle, nor do they have the specialized training required to effectively produce significant change in the ASD adult's life out in the social world. Allow me to explain my view in more detail.

To begin, let me first start off by stating that I believe therapy is wonderful for neurotypicals (people who do not have ASD or an Autism Spectrum Disorder). I am a trained therapist and I know that therapeutic techniques are highly effective. The problem for me arose when I realized that all of the skills and techniques that I was eagerly learning in class did not help in my own relationship with my husband. In fact, the techniques and advice would often have the opposite or completely unexpected result when implemented in my own life. This is when I began to realize my husband may fit the textbook definition of what was then called Asperger's Syndrome.

All I knew in my graduate training was the textbook definition of Asperger's Syndrome. There were no classes on Autism, Asperger's, PDD:NOS, or what we now collectively call Autism Spectrum Disorders. Likewise, there were no formal courses on any of the learning disabilities, only the definitions and brief overviews in graduate level abnormal psychology courses. To this day, curriculums for therapists still do not necessarily include ASD courses. We have a community of therapists who are the only professionals covered by insurance companies to work with our ASD population, and they have no formal extensive training in ASD, nor do they have the knowledge of the real-life experiences these individuals and families go through. This instilled a powerful sense of disappointment in the profession I had chosen, and I was overcome with a great desire to make a change using my education and real world experience. I never pursued my therapy license and instead obtained multiple certifications in autism. I went on to start my own Life Coaching company where I wouldn't engage in traditional therapy, rather, I would teach real-life skills including social skills, communication skills, independent living, and college/career development. I would also come to realize that there would be a heavy focus on non-verbal communication training as well as healthy relationship building, executive functioning, and much more.

My certifications are from the International Board of Credentialing and Continuing Education Standards. As of 2001, they formed the belief that we needed some kind of standardizing cognitive disorder education through all realms including healthcare, education, and corporate environments. They have and continue to develop the industry standards, and I stand by what they are accomplishing. As of this moment, I have both the Advanced Certified Autism Specialist Level 2 Certification as well as the Board Certified Cognitive Specialist Certification. These credentials help me to stay relevant in ASD and cognitive disorder research, allowing me to better serve my clients.

What you will notice with this training is that ASD is a social and communicative disorder, and a great deal of what I do includes a heavy focus on non-verbal communication training. For instance, I work with the majority of my client base on things like body language and purposeful eye contact. The nuances of social communication are so highly complex and are not learned as intuitively by many on the Autism Spectrum. There are very few people and organizations that understand this discrepancy. Most do not realize how the current treatment options focus mostly on medical and academic areas rather than understanding the complexities of the social area that neurotypicals learn much more naturally. Furthermore, in my work, there is a heavy focus on healthy relationship building. Forming relationships, ones that are healthy and safe, are huge determinants in finding success and contentment in life, more so than any other talent or ability, and I believe those talents and abilities often get overlooked if we are not able to communicate our abilities and potential effectively.

In this book, I will go into detail about all of my methods with the hope that Life Coaching for ASD children and adults becomes part of the norm in terms of supplementing the current evidence-based approaches and treatments we have for social disorders. I've seen the progress and growth in hundreds of clients, and my dream is to see that change on a much larger scale. My greatest hope is that this book not only helps an individual on the spectrum, a parent, an entire family, and raises awareness, but also helps the professionals out there who work with this population of people on a daily basis to see that there is a way to teach these intricacies and understand how much of an impact it can have on each of our client's lives.

PART 1: FOR THE ASD ADULT

Expectations, Problems and Solutions

FOREWORD

Matthew Hoel, MBA

I have always described my experience with Aspergers much like having an instruction manual inside your mind that is "all about yourself." The manual is perfect. It tells you exactly what to do, when you need to do it, and how much effort will be required. You refer to this manual for everything and it never fails you... except when it does. You see, if your instruction manual says you prefer ice in your drink, and the waiter comes by and gives you one without ice, an alarm inside your brain begins blaring and the only way you can get rid of it is if you get your drink *with ice*!

To make matters more complicated, my instruction manual doesn't have a very detailed section about dealing with other people. That would be fine if we could just live in complete isolation. However, because humans are social animals, and we all (directly or indirectly) depend on each other for survival, having instructional manuals without that section on "dealing with people" makes it that much more difficult to satisfy our desires.

I first began seeking services from Jaclyn back in 2015. I was 23, beginning my bachelors degree at the University of Minnesota Duluth, and I was probably the loneliest person on Earth. My instruction manual made it exceptionally difficult for me to interact with anyone that did not have the same interests as I did. As a result, my social circle was limited, and my confidence was reduced dramatically. I strongly desired a romantic relationship but lacked the social skills, experience, or confidence to hold one longer than a couple months. My biggest fear was that all my social flaws were genetic and it would be impossible for me to build relationships or live a happy life.

I felt that a life coach that understood Aspergers would help me with not only interpreting other people, but also allow me to expand my own instruction manual. Within the first few weeks of speaking with Jaclyn, I realized she was far more than just a therapist. She was a problem solver. Every time I found myself stressed out or needed to find the answer to something, Jaclyn had a solution for me. It was like having someone there that you could constantly bounce ideas off of. She took interest in the same things I did and she actually did her research on those topics — everything from animes that I liked to job openings in my hometown. It was clear to me after our first few sessions together that she was providing me a valuable service that I had been missing for most of my life. She was genuinely invested in my success and happiness.

It was through her services that I was able to gain confidence in myself. She first helped me find, control, and utilize my sense of "focus" (that many people on the spectrum have) for my own benefits. I gained an interest in fitness and nutrition that allowed me to lose 40lbs and get into the best shape of my life. I started to go out more in public, initiated conversations with total strangers, made friends with them, and ultimately began dating.

Dating was especially hard for me because it required me to be adaptable and pay attention to the smallest details. I once ruined a movie date because I couldn't find the right seat in the theater. On another, I dropped the "R word" in front of someone who works with special needs kids (Jaclyn has fortunately helped remove this word from my vocabulary entirely). I've misinterpreted women who were looking for something serious and plenty more who were looking for something temporary. But with every heartbreak and mishap, my life coach was there to assure me that some things just weren't so much my fault and that they just weren't meant to be.

It was shortly after this point when Jaclyn had assisted me through probably the most difficult moments of my life — I had been going out with an international freshman student from

Nepal for a few weeks and had fallen madly in love with her. Unlike previous women I had dated, this girl was incredibly sweet, caring, and, most of all, patient with my Aspergers. Having culture shock can often times be an equivalent experience to being on the spectrum, and I believe this dynamic helped her to look more closely at the intent behind my actions rather than take things I did or said at face value. I also felt that she was simply someone who had the kind of love and patience you could build a long-term relationship with, regardless of the types of challenges you would face together. Even if we didn't have that many common interests, that ability to love and be loved was unique and something that I valued more than anything else in this world.

When she told me that she would be moving back to her extended family in New York City, I was devastated. I knew that what we had was special. I wanted to do everything in my power to keep her with me, but her situation was far more complicated than anything I had anticipated. While having a long-distance relationship was quite possible, it would likely be too difficult to maintain due to how little time she would have between work and school. Our relationship would be over as soon as she moved back. After a lot of deliberation, I decided to do the most logical thing... and marry her! Jaclyn, of course, helped me understand how crazy that idea was, but she could also see how special this girl was compared to all the others I dated. She saw first-hand the challenges I had to overcome to get to this point and knew I was ready to take on whatever life was ready to throw at me. So, Jaclyn gave me another option, and together, we were able to come up with an acceptable arrangement.

Jaclyn's services didn't stop there. My girlfriend eventually turned into my wife and I came to the very beautiful (and scary) realization that my life was no longer just my own; I'm permanently sharing it with another human being. That's especially tough when you're on the spectrum, because you're so particular about how you do things that you're now forcing yourself to make compromises at times to make room for that other person's life inside of your own. Jaclyn explained it best when she told me that my wife isn't someone who I can just put up on a shelf when I'm done with her. She's now stapled onto my instruction manual, for better or worse.

While I admit there are plenty of struggles with being married on the spectrum, I know that life in general has its ups and downs that we all must ride through. That's why I strongly feel that having a life coach (especially if you are on the spectrum) is essential to having a successful life. They can help you navigate an unfamiliar and stressful situation in a way that simultaneously protects yourself and allows you to achieve your goals. They can act like your compass when your instruction manual doesn't have the answers. They can walk you through the blank pages of your instruction manual or mind, teach you how to do it on your own and explain to you why it's all important. They can help you unlock your true potential and help you harness it to make your life better than you ever thought possible. *That* is what a life coach actually does, and getting services from one was easily the best decision I've ever made.

CHAPTER 1

The High School Years

While symptoms of ASD are apparent at a very young age, it is common for those differences to begin to cause distress at the start of high school. This is typically why we are usually open to begin working with high school students in order to help transition them into the adult world. The reason high school can sometimes become challenging for a child on the spectrum is because that is the point where social communication and expectation becomes highly complex. I often have parents tell me that everything in elementary school and even middle school was going well, when suddenly, high school seemed to cause everything to go downhill. With the complex social demands of high school comes increasing academic demands, more personal responsibilities, varied and unpredictably changing environments, and puberty. Additionally, there is the stress of finding and maintaining friendships, possibly dating, discovering one's sexuality, and dealing with bullies.

Over the course of four years, a young adult on the spectrum will be focused on mastering this very specific yet convoluted environment. Then, when he or she comes close to understanding how to navigate this isolated world, they are then thrust into a new and even larger world with a completely new set of societal expectations. Now, of course, this is not true for every individual on the spectrum. Some clients have had horrible experiences all throughout their school careers while others have the fondest of memories. On average, I have found the social demands and struggles for those on the spectrum typically occur around this time. So, it is important to discuss why this is occurring for young adults on the spectrum and how we can work to improve their high school experience.

The biggest priority most schools and parents have is a child's academic achievement. I believe this focus should be shifted, for all students, to a social precedence. The biggest predictor of success in life is not your academic ability; rather, it is your ability to interact with society effectively. Many of my clients have achieved great things academically, but when it is time to get a job or begin a career, they fall short because of their lack of a social education. A Master's degree does not automatically get you a job. The ability to relate to and connect with people is what gets us opportunities in this world. I could have all of the knowledge in the world, but if I could not communicate that knowledge to prospective clients, I would fail as a Life Coach. Similarly, if I had all of the mathematical knowledge in the world, it would not matter in terms of my career if my boss found it to be easier to communicate with someone who had lesser math knowledge. The social and communicative aspects are just as, if not more, valuable than the academic. What this means is that high schools must begin incorporating social classes and opportunities for all students, not just those on the spectrum. Everyone is struggling socially these days in a world taken over by social media, text messaging, and a lack of proper one-to-one and group communication opportunities. Now, many schools will tell you that they do have social skills classes, but the reality is that they are nowhere near as detailed and thorough as they need to be for our young adults on the ASD Spectrum. There is absolutely no social curriculum in schools developed by ASD experts and leaders in the field. This is the main reason why so many clients come to us in the first place — they have had little to no training in the nuances of social communication.

As such, the ASD Adult student and, quite frankly, all students can benefit from a detailed social curriculum. In my experience, a proper program must include social skills for each level of intimacy you share with an individual or group. If no such curriculum is available to you, there are certainly ways to teach yourself. The first step towards learning a new concept is to first understand the theory behind what you are learning. Next comes putting what you have learned into real world practice, and lastly, you successfully demonstrate adequate knowledge and performance of that learned concept. Levels range from a first meeting with a new acquaintance to very close familial relationships. Each level, starting with the lowest (Level 1 acquaintances), has clear cut rules, requirements, and boundaries that can be taught in-depth and practiced in simulation and real-world situations. For instance, Level 1 is the lowest level, where people you interact with are labeled as an acquaintance. It is the bottom level of a friendship pyramid (see appendix), where small talk is the primary form of interaction. Being at the bottom of the pyramid, this level of friendship should hold the most number of people in your life. Therefore, small talk is the main social skill that must be worked on in order to master the first level of friendship, which is the solid base for every other type of friendship that follows. Small talk involves immediate environmental commonalities. Many of my clients on the spectrum despise small talk because it seemingly holds little meaning. The reality is that small talk is actually an indicator that those who engage have a genuine desire to interact with each other. The problem is that intimacy at this level is so low that the only safe topics of conversation are immediately in the environment. It isn't about the topics you choose at this stage; rather, it is about recognizing when someone would like to interact with you at the acquaintance level, and your ability to respond appropriately to indicate that you would like to interact as well. Small talk is not meant to be torture. It is a tool you utilize to begin a friendship. How far that relationship progresses will vary considerably from person to person.

Now we must put the theory of the small talk phase into practice in the real world. Let's say you are in a coffee shop and would like to speak to the cashier you see each morning. She fits the criteria of an acquaintance because you see her each day but your relationship does not extend beyond that circumstance. It is the morning, so a greeting of "good morning" is very appropriate in this situation. You are attempting to be friendly, so indicating friendliness through the tone of your voice and with a smile on your face gives clear non-verbal indicators to the cashier that you are engaging her in a positive way. You can practice your friendly tone of voice by recording yourself on your cell phone and video recording yourself on your phone so that you can see how you come off to the outside world, and then you can fine-tune what looks and feels most natural and appropriate. You can also enlist the assistance of a family member or your life coach to help you with this process.

Once you greet the cashier successfully, the ball is now in her court. This is an analogy that illustrates that it is now time for the cashier to respond to you. No further action is required on your part until the cashier responds. There are exceptions to this, such as if the cashier did not hear you or there was an interruption of some kind. However, most of the time, you will be awaiting a response. This response can come in a variety of ways. One, they can return the greeting in a positive, neutral, or dismissive way. You must use that information to decide your next move. If it is positive, you may proceed with further inter-action. Positive responses include a happy tone of voice, a smile, and a return greeting. On the other hand, if the response is neu-tral, you may wish to proceed with caution because the cashier may be too busy, distracted, or disinterested in interacting at this time. If the reaction is dismissive, you should always back off and make an attempt at a later date. A string of dismissive re-sponses or lack of responses is an indicator that this person does not want to interact with you, and that is okay! It does not mean it is a personal rejection. It simply implies that this person does not feel like being social, and that is her prerogative. Besides a greeting, the cashier can also respond with a question such as, "How are you today?" This is an excellent opportunity for you to say a little more than just "fine." You could respond by say-ing, "I am well because it is such a beautiful day outside." If you end your response there, you are leaving it to the other person to respond in either an open or closed format. If they want the conversation to continue, they will say more or ask more questions. If they want the conversation to end, they will most likely acknowledge your response verbally or non-verbally and go on with their day. Either way, you have successfully engaged in a short period of small talk.

Small talk is generally short but could go on for quite some time depending on how eager the participants are to converse. Once you are able to engage in small talk such as this in a variety of environments, situations, and times throughout the day with various acquaintances, you will have mastered the level of small talk and will most likely be able to generalize those skills to similar small talk situations. You then move up the relationship pyramid and continue to teach yourself how to engage with people at every level through learning the theory, engaging in real world practice, and successfully demonstrating your new found skill. Let us now continue our focus on high school with a discussion about why many people on the spectrum begin to struggle through these elaborate social years.

As I mentioned earlier, the biggest focus in high school for the school system and many parents is doing well academically and getting high grades. With high school comes increasing academic responsibilities. The workload and class difficulty increases exponentially from middle school to high school. Many ASD students welcome the academic challenges, while others struggle because of all the other pressures they are experiencing socially. So, you take a highly intelligent ASD student who, in the past, was generally great at academics but begins to struggle because of varying and increasing social demands, and you take away something that they identified themselves with — being smart. Now you have a young man or woman who has always felt intelligent but is now struggling in that realm too. The blow to one's self-confidence in this situation can be intense. Now, this is not the experience of every student on the spectrum because many continue to do well academically and others have always struggled with certain courses. No two clients are the same, but I find it important to talk in averages and what I see often in my work. I urge the reader not to take everything I say as a definitive problem or symptom of ASD, but to recognize these possibilities when working with someone on the spectrum rather than making assumptions such as the student is "lazy" or "difficult" or "uninterested." If a student was previously succeeding academically and that suddenly changes in a new environment or situation, such as the transition to high school, then we must look at all the possibilities for that change. The goal here is to bring awareness and recognition as to why these increased academic demands contribute to the ASD student's struggles.

Let's say, for instance, you are a strong student academically. Your favorite course is history. In this hypothetical example, you usually do quite well in your history courses, but this year, the teacher has put a very strong emphasis on group projects. You are expected by your teacher, parents, and other students in your group to perform well academically in this particular class as you have done in previous years. However, the social demands of the group projects are putting a strain on your ability to perform academically. You are having a difficult time participating in the group discussions and knowing when it is appropriate to be a leader or a follower. You may also have anxiety when talking to others, and in the group setting, that feeling of anxiety is magnified. Each student in the group has differing ways of working on the project, and the confusion of who is doing what is causing you to get extremely frustrated. After all, you have to rely on everyone working together in order to obtain a passing grade. What do you do in a situation with so many variables and convoluted problems that are causing you distress? A client of mine went through this very scenario. He was frustrated because the due date for the project was fast approaching but the group had not yet discussed an action plan. He decided to take the lead so that the project could progress. Sadly, the group did not like his choices for the project and they rejected his ideas. He then shut down and lost interest in working with the group.

Luckily, he was still able to pass the class, but he did not learn anything in terms of the academic material or the social experience of the group setting.

There are many options here. The most important advice I can give you in this difficult situation is to not allow too much time to go by before you take action. These are the times when advocating for yourself is most important. Asking for help when you need it, as mentioned earlier, is the number one predictor of success in life. This is a case where asking for help is paramount. One, you go to your teacher and/or IEP team and discuss your struggles with the group environment. You ask for tools and support to help get you through this difficult social situation. Sometimes this will work and you will have enough support to get through the experience. It is my experience, however, that students rarely get the support they need in these group scenarios. So when asking for help from your resources does not prove fruitful, you now need to actively look for alternatives to a difficult situation. One possibility is that you can ask for an individual assignment as an accommodation while also participating in the group activities. Perhaps asking the group to communicate with you in ways that are more comfortable for you, such as email or text message, may prove useful. The biggest takeaway here is the value of seeking out solutions from a trusted external source. This is a skill that you will need throughout your entire life. Learning, practicing, and mastering this skill now will serve you through the whole of your adult life. Still, this does not solve the group project issue in an ideal way. In my experience, there are very few ideal solutions. I feel many of the evidence-based approaches to the social environment for ASD adults fails them by making it seem like there is always a clear-cut answer to a situation. My answer to that is there isn't always a clear-cut satisfying answer; however, there is always an answer that will be good enough to accomplish what you need to accomplish in order to move on with your life.

Besides academic demands, there are also more personal responsibilities expected of a student in high school. For instance, a student is expected to do more at home on their own. Some parents may laugh at that statement and think, "What are you talking about? They do nothing at home!" However, the reason many do "nothing" at home is because they are so drained from dealing with the school day. Likewise, there are many other reasons home demands are not being met, but in my professional opinion, the main reason that responsibilities aren't being accomplished at home is because the young adult on the spectrum is overwhelmed and shutting down. The reason they are shutting down is not because of the home demands but because of the combination of life demands from both school and home. Home is thought of as the safe haven to escape the pressures of society. So when a young adult is not meeting the expectations of the home environment, I always examine that environment as well as the outside environments that are influencing that person's productivity and well-being.

A common expectation for many at home is the ability to keep their room clean. Keeping a room clean often involves making the bed, arranging items neatly on shelves and in storage, keeping a clear floor, and maintaining and a dust-free, sanitary environment. After a long day at school, a student may come home to a parent who is demanding that they clean their room. This is a task that may seem daunting when the chore hasn't been maintained for a long period of time. A simple daily or weekly task becomes a huge undertaking. This huge undertaking, after a long day at school, can produce enormous amounts of stress. The parental expectation is a clean room. The problem is that the child does not have the energy or mental stamina to undertake such a large project during that time period. The solution lies in breaking up this project into smaller pieces. Again, self-advocacy skills come into play here. An arrangement with the parents where the child works on 1-2 room cleaning chores for 10 minutes a day is a reasonable and doable request — especially when compared to cleaning the entire room at once, which, in some cases, could take a few hours. Day 1: the child makes her bed before leaving for school. The task takes 3 minutes. Upon returning from school, the child has 7 minutes to perform another room cleaning task. Perhaps this day is appropriate to take all the dirty laundry on the floor to the laundry room. The next day, the child makes her bed and takes any additional dirty laundry to the laundry room. The task takes 4 minutes before school which leaves 6 minutes of room cleaning time upon her return home. The next task to tackle is arranging the papers on her desk so that she has room to work on her school assignments. The task takes 6 minutes and her room chores for the day are complete. This continues for a week, and a small time investment each day ultimately proves to be a large accomplishment over the course of a week. Now the child simply has to maintain the clean room by dedicating 10 minutes or less a day to maintenance. That small amount of time can easily be added to a schedule and this method can be applied to almost any previously neglected life demand.

On occasion, parents are surprised that when I, as the coach, instruct my clients to do a task, such as clean their room, there is almost immediate progress. This is frustrating for parents who have been telling their child to clean their room for months, if not years, on end. The difference is how you present the request. The key to any of us accomplishing a large project is to break it down into small, doable pieces. For the neurotypical mind, that is easier to do than for someone on the ASD spectrum. An ASD individual feeling the pressures of a life demand that is too overwhelming may simply just shut down due to being overloaded. The best way to solve this issue is to learn the process of breaking down larger tasks into smaller, more reasonable pieces, rather than the larger expectations of your family, friends or other professionals. This can be difficult to do on your own, and a life coach can help you initially learn that process of breaking things down into smaller and smaller steps until you find a step that is most comfortable for you. In the room cleaning example, for instance, it may be too big of a step for you to make your bed completely in one go. We may have to first work on tucking in the sheets each morning before school and finishing making the bed upon your return. One thing about learning a new process is that as we do it more, we get quicker at accomplishing it. It becomes automatic over time, similar to learning to drive a car. So, eventually, we go from tucking in the sheets in the morning to tucking in the sheets and smoothing out the blanket in the morning, and then all you need to do is fluff and arrange the pillows when you get home from school. Showing your parents that you are following steps and making progress towards a goal is always better than shutting down and giving up. It doesn't have to be as simple as making your bed. In fact, this theory can be applied to any task that requires your attention to completion. And remember, if you are unsure of what to do, ask someone to help you create the smaller steps that will lead you to big success.

Going back to the high school environment, we see that compared to middle and elementary schools, there are also much more frequently changing classes. A student with ASD gets comfortable with a classroom and the daily routine, but in high school, that routine can be disrupted quite frequently. The need to change environments and figure out the expectations of multiple social environments can cause distress for someone who struggles with shifting so quickly and so often. So now we have a student who is stressed because of increased academic demands, increased personal responsibilities, and navigating multiple and frequently changing environments. The expectation here is being able to deal with changing classes frequently throughout the day; however, the problem is that for this particular individual that shift is extremely difficult. Again, self-advocacy can be utilized here. I had a client who was much better able to succeed academically when his environment stayed stable. This particular student was able to self teach, and he frequently did his work in a study hall instead of going through the stressors of changing classes all day long. This was established by speaking with his parents, his IEP team, and working with his teachers to make sure he was accomplishing and learning all that the curriculum required while allowing him the flexibility to do that work in an environment where he could succeed. He was then able to get his socialization time in during lunch, gym class, and his other extracurricular activities. This is just one possible solution for this particular client, and there are a multitude of other possibilities for students with differing needs. The idea here is to identify the expectation, the problem, and then come up with individualized solutions.

We also have to remember that there are other students that this young adult is struggling to interact with and form friendships with, another highly complex social task. The majority of my clients suffer from lack of friendships and social circles. They repeatedly try to form friendships and either get rejected or essentially fail to connect with their peers. This pattern creates a struggling student who is now extremely lonely. One of the toughest issues to tackle is when a student is lacking friendships and feeling extremely lonely. Loneliness is an epidemic in today's society, not only for those on the spectrum. What can the high school student do to help him develop friendships and keep loneliness at bay? Many turn to online friendships. These friendships are just as valid and real as in-person relationships. I encourage these friendships and value the impact they have in a person's life. Still, we want to have a balance of virtual and real-life friendships. As we discussed earlier, high school is a very complex time socially. Students are experimenting and learning how to interact during this time. There is a lot of drama, a lot of gossip, and cliques tend to form. How does a student who is a culture of one learn how to integrate with an established friendship circle?

A client of mine utilized his family resources to help establish friendships both inside and outside of school. His father was a musician and entertainer and his mother was a social butterfly. Together, they arranged to have parties and gatherings at their home and off-site where everyone in this client's class was invited. Through his parents' support, he was able to make many friends throughout his high school years because there were opportunities created to do so. Make your own opportunities. Start a club, join an already established organization or sports team, use your home support to have people over or to go on field trips. Likewise, utilize your IEP team to help you create situations where socialization can occur safely and successfully. When I was in high school, there was a wonderful program called "Peer Leadership." I always regret not participating in that program because I saw how close the students became during their time together. These students were from all walks of life, often from a wide variety of social groups and backgrounds. Another important thing to remember is to not be afraid of solitude. Solitude is not loneliness. Solitude is an enjoyable experience where you take time for yourself, your own ultimate relationship, and nurture your connection to your inner experience.

As an aside to the topic of loneliness, I frequently speak online to an extremely lonely young woman. She cannot afford coaching and is not in my local area, but I have made time to chat with her from time to time over the years. She is very much isolated from the social world. This is a woman in her early 40s who has had a rough relationship with her parents, whom she has lived with for her entire life. Her siblings and extended family members rarely interact with her. When they do, it is often an unpleasant experience. She is most often alone and suffering. She has no friendships and has been through countless therapists, counselors, and psychologists who have not been capable of helping her achieve socialization. These professionals simply do not have the skills or ability to teach socialization. It breaks my heart that there are so many people like this young woman who have absolutely no support. There is nothing for her. She has been abused, ridiculed, and bullied for her entire life. I have been doing my best from a distance to attempt to find this girl a social shadow, a program that is free for her to participate in — anything that will help her progress socially and alleviate her loneliness. It is my great hope that we can one day end loneliness for everyone. So remember, if you have tools at your disposal to help yourself get out of the depths of loneliness, make sure you utilize them. There are many out there who do not even have that, and we need to do our best to get those tools to as many people as we possibly can. This brings me to the topic of bullying.

When a student is struggling to make friendships and form a peer group, they are exposed to potential bullying. I would say that almost all of the clients I work with have been bullied at some point in their lives, both as students and adults. Bullying can happen to anyone, but it is much more likely to occur if you do not have the protection of a social group. A lone target is often the choice for a bully, especially one who can recognize the struggles and sufferings of someone on the ASD spectrum — in other words, someone who does not have enough social knowledge to effectively defend him or herself. The emotional and psychological toll of being bullied can cause so much distress that we can see why so many on the spectrum seem to give up. They become labeled as "lazy" or "lacking motivation," when the reality is that they are exhausted, drained, pulled in too many directions, and are not being taught the skills they need to actually succeed in these situations.

How do you succeed against a bully? The majority of the bullying stories I hear rarely have a positive outcome. Usually, the success comes much later, after the bullying has occurred. I attended a 20-year high school reunion. It was not my reunion, but I was there observing. I noticed how the students that struggled in high school ended up being some of the most successful adults. Someone there introduced me to one of the most popular and attractive guys in the school at the time. Sadly, he did not make much of himself and was struggling to find a long-term relationship. The high school strugglers, on the other hand, mainly were married with multiple children and had obtained successful and fruitful careers. At one point in the evening, I saw a man walk up and announce to the group that he had just confronted his high school bully. He was ecstatic, proud, and empowered. After 20 years, he built a life for himself but still carried the burden and trauma of his bully. That day, I saw a person transform and heal the damage of the past all on his own. It was no longer about what the bully did to him, but what that person had done with his life despite that bully's interference. It was a beautiful moment. That story may help someone whose bullying occurred in the past, even though it may not be as helpful to someone currently going through it. When dealing with a bully, the most important thing is to learn how to stay emotionally healthy. The bully is emotionally damaged and attempts to equally damage his or her victim. I have found that a person who is bullied has two options: become a bully or overcome the bullying. Most bullies are the victims of bullying or abuse. This is almost always the case. They are people that we should pity, and the best way to rise above their actions is to keep ourselves healthy, sane, and protected. No one should have to go through being bullied, so self-advocacy is a must. Do not be afraid to report your bully to your parents, a trusted teacher, your IEP team, a friend, a relative, or anyone in a position of authority. You have a right to be both physically and emotionally safe. There are no easy answers when it comes to bullies in the world. However, one thing is clear — a bully will not get far, while you will soar towards your fullest potential as long as you never give up.

I am not even close to being done discussing the struggles and demands put on a student with ASD. What I am trying to do here is paint a picture of what these young men and women experience so that neurotypicals, or the average person, can understand what students with ASD are experiencing. Rather than simply labeling them with a disorder and putting them on medications, we should actually consider providing skills and knowledge that will help them navigate and succeed in these situations. For example, I am terrible at mathematics. No one has labeled me with a disability because I have no natural ability to do math. What happens is when I need to learn math, I sit down with someone who is proficient at math, and they teach me how to do that math problem, step-by-step, until I understand and can generalize my knowledge to other similar math problems. I may not ever become a mathematician, but I will certainly learn enough math to get by in life. The same is true for my clients. They may never be the most social people in the world, but they can certainly learn if someone sits down with them and teaches them the skills they are lacking, rather than brushing them off and telling parents their child will never amount to anything.

Now, let's get back to discussing the other pressures of high school. These pressures have an effect on all students, but they particularly affect our ASD clients due to the complex social intricacies interwoven into all of these experiences. One such struggle is hitting puberty. The bodily and hormonal changes that an ASD student struggles with processing and understanding can be difficult to work through due to a mind/body disconnect. Many on the spectrum do not sense their bodies in the same way a neurotypical might. Likewise, they may be hypersensitive to certain stimuli and internal experiences.

I have had multiple clients struggle with puberty during our coaching time together. One client actually went through puberty much later than expected. Notably, some with autism develop more slowly than their peers. In fact, this client's teeth even came in later than his typically developing peers. So, when he was finally going through puberty, his peers were mostly already finished. This caused distress and confusion during a pivotal time in his high school career. If you're still going through puberty, it can make transitioning out of high school into the adult world extremely daunting. Another client of mine was a female who was always very sweet and gentle, but she got very aggressive and angry during her pubescent years. After much coaching, therapy, and medical visits, we came up with a plan of action to put her on an oral contraceptive that significantly reduced her puberty symptoms, allowing her to put the biological issues aside and focus on the social issues at hand. I always feel the best way to deal with a biological function or anything we do not have any control over is to be as informed and prepared as possible before that change occurs. This allows us to make rational and informed plans that are much easier to carry out when the mind is in the midst of it. I did not have access to these clients before puberty hit, so I could not explain and prepare them for what to expect, I was still able to explain as things were occurring to help alleviate their distress. There are wonderful books and resources online and at your local library that discuss puberty and what to expect during this time. Reading up on bodily changes and what most people experience can certainly make a difference in your life as it happens. Speaking with your coach, medical professional, and your parents is also an excellent way to find out what to expect during this chaotic hormonal time period. Still, your experience may be quite different from the experience of a neurotypical peer. That is perfectly normal for you. It is also something that is temporary. Puberty is a difficult time for most of us, but it may be magnified for someone on the spectrum who is already struggling with a mind/body disconnect. Using this time to meditate, engage in self-care, and finding ways to communicate your discomfort to your team in order to come up with helpful solutions are all tools that you can utilize to help you get through this biologically confusing time.

Following puberty, the desire for closeness and romantic relationships starts to arise. Feelings of loneliness can be magnified after puberty because of the strong desire for closeness and companionship in addition to sexual desires. It is true that some clients have no interest in romantic relationships, while others want it more than anything else in the world. They want to date but find it nearly impossible when they already struggle with finding friendships. We tend to find romantic relationships through friendship circles, and many clients don't have those established groups to encounter a potential romantic partner.

So what do you do when you don't have access to traditional methods of meeting a potential romantic partner? Where and how do people meet in today's world? Well, since we are talking about high school, that is typically the meeting place we have to work with. People often become attracted to each other when participating in some sort of common activity or interest. When I was in high school, I noticed people in the drama department often began dating each other as the school year went on. One of those relationships has lasted until this very day, along with the addition of children and a wide circle of familial and friendship support. The commonalities we share with people in a school club or organization could lead to a potential romantic relationship. However, if you are looking for a specific gender, such as a female, and your club of interest is something like anime, your interest has the potential to not attract as many females. Don't get me wrong, there are many females who love anime, but there is a chance that anime could be a male dominated club. If there does happen to be one or two females in that particular club, they will be highly sought after and competition will run high. It is best to be flexible and willing to take on (or at the very least learn about) a variety of interests so that you may be exposed to a greater pool of potential romantic interests. For example, I once convinced a male client to attend a local yoga class mostly dominated by women. While it was intimidating at first, he quickly realized that yoga increased his physicality and also exposed him to a great deal of female attention. While he did not find a girlfriend at this class, he was still able to make friends and grow his self-confidence in terms of becoming more at ease when speaking to women. A few years later, he met a wonderful young women on an online dating app, and they have been happily together ever since. My advice is to not feel hopeless if you struggle with making friends and establishing yourself in a clique. Instead, go out and make opportunities for yourself at school or outside of school. In that way, you can gain experience and confidence that will serve you well when the right person does come along. These days, that can be in the form of joining or starting a club, sport, or organization at school, or using online tools such as meetup.com and community tools at the local library or community center to create opportunities outside of school. Do not allow yourself to be boxed in by what's available if you need something more. Likewise, if you struggle to do this on your own, you can enlist the help of your parents, siblings, life coach, or anyone on your team to create a plan of action that will assist you in making your vision a reality. Remember, the biggest predictor of success in life is your ability to ask for help when you need it.

Another struggle is understanding sexuality and your identity as a person. This is something everyone works through, but it is even more difficult if someone is isolated and lonely. Remember, not all people on the spectrum are isolated or lonely, but many are, so I address it here because it is important to recognize and understand it so that we can work to improve it. Many young adults on the spectrum have come to me and my team of coaches because they are struggling with their sexuality and personal identity. This is not something we can figure out for you, but we can certainly guide you along your path to self-understanding. Understanding ourselves is something we all struggle with, especially in the high school years. This can be even more difficult when you are on the spectrum. You may not even fully discover yourself during these years. Some people take longer than others to figure out their truest self. Those on the spectrum often work very hard to discover and understand the rules of society. Many try to master societal rules in order to fit in. I think neurotypicals have a very strong desire to fit in, and when they are confident and strong enough, they eventually make a conscious choice to defy society in order to be true to themselves and their identity. In contrast, someone on the spectrum may also desire to fit in, but they might still be struggling to understand the rules of society, let alone how they could effectively and successfully break that barrier. My rules are simple. We are who we are as long as we do not break society's *laws* — not just any laws but the big ones. No murder, no assault, no violence, no stealing, and never *intentionally* harming another person. Be who you feel you are, even if it goes against society's "rules," just as long as you respect basic laws. Trust your gut. This is something I tell all of my clients. Your gut or instincts are intact. Society may disagree with your instincts, your mind and body might struggle with processing speed and accuracy, but your gut knows who you are as a person. It may take some time to learn how to communicate that to yourself and others, but you will get there. It is important to not be afraid of that. There is room in society for everyone. A life coach or trusted adult can guide you on this journey and should never tell you what to do. A good coach's job is to help you make the choices you want to make with the top priority of helping you make wise and safe decisions along the way.

Besides the social issues I've discussed above, there are also the practical issues of learning to drive a car and transitioning out of high school to either college or some sort of job or career. One of the first questions I ask a parent or potential client is if they drive. The goal of life coaching adults on the ASD spectrum is to get them to be as independent as possible, and driving is one of those markers of freedom and independence in our society. Not all clients can drive, so there are alternatives that we work on such as public transportation, or moving to an area where they can mostly walk or take alternative forms of transportation. Some clients struggle with the written test, so I urge them to use different study methods such as downloading the instructional manual's audio version to help with absorbing the material. Other clients get anxious and find it difficult to perform during the road test. I urge parents to provide as many practice opportunities as possible, and I also suggest taking driving lessons with teachers experienced and understanding of the unique needs of an individual with ASD. Still other clients have trouble with reaction time, as well as reliably handling all of the mechanical as well as social rules of the road. In cases like these, I urge parents to seek a local driving simulator to help their young adult practice driving safely before hitting the real pavement. Some may not be able to drive safely enough to obtain a license, but I do encourage all of my clients to try. Many are surprised at what they can accomplish if they give it a chance with the proper accommodations put into place.

Lastly, transitioning out of high school is another pressure put on the student that can cause significant distress. Test preparations, extended standardized testing, college applications, job applications, fears of living on their own or with a roommate, what to study in college or what kind of job to seek out, taking care of one's basic needs, and ultimately leaving an environment that the student has spent the last 4 years attempting to master is terrifying when you have no visual concept of what comes next. Many of my clients do not see what the majority of people can picture in their minds about the future or a new situation. Some clients are happy to see high school end and a new chapter begin, while others can barely see that there is another page to turn. This is why I spend significant amounts of time preparing students for the transition out of high school into either college or the job world.

Transitioning out of high school into the adult world is a complex process that needs to begin as early as possible in a child's high school years. What I often see is by the time a student finishes high school, they have mastered the high school environment, but they have little preparation regarding the expectations of the much larger world to follow. It is important to leave high school with a few important skills, and these skills are not academic. In order to succeed in the real world, you must know how to manage yourself. You need to be able to get yourself up in the morning, either on your own or with the assistance of some sort of alarm. In order to function in society effectively, you need to be able to keep yourself clean and well-groomed on a consistent and regular basis. Additionally, you must be able to perform a slew of executive functioning skills to run your day on your own or with the assistance of a calendar or other type of organizational system. These skills include cleaning your space, being capable of shopping, feeding and clothing yourself, getting to your appointments and meeting your daily responsibilities, budgeting time and money, communicating effectively with everyone you come in contact with throughout the course of a day, having a bit of fun, and most importantly, asking for help when you need it. If you can manage your life inside and outside of school, and not just what high school expects during those hours, you are well on your way to being able to tackle anything that life throws at you out in the real world.

In the next three chapters, I will discuss the experiences and struggles of those worlds just as I have in this chapter about high school. The second part of this book will then get into more detail about life coaching and how it can help an adult on ASD spectrum effectively work through the struggles of these realms to ultimately reach a point of success and contentment in their life.

CHAPTER 2

The College and University Experience

In the previous chapter, I briefly touched upon the idea that many ASD adults cannot see the future in the same way a neurotypical adult can envision one. In my work, I have come to the realization that I can see things in my mind's eye that many of my clients have not yet developed on their own. For instance, some of my clients have a fear of traveling. As I mentioned before, not all people on the spectrum have a fear of travel. The purpose of this example is to attempt to illustrate the differences between the autistic mind and the neurotypical mind in terms of seeing and predicting the future. So, a client who is afraid of traveling may get anxious for a variety of reasons. One of those reasons could be previous negative traveling experiences. However, I have found that many clients get anxious when traveling to a new place because they cannot see all the steps in-between to get to the final destination. Even if I haven't been somewhere before, as a neurotypical, I can imagine the car ride to the airport, and I have a general image of what the airport looks like on the inside and out, a general knowledge of walking through security and how I am expected to act in that situation, an idea of how long I will be waiting in line and for my flight, and I will also be prepared for a few "unexpected" issues such as a delayed flight or a sudden illness. My neurotypical mind has an incredible ability to prepare me for a variety of social situations on the fly. The ASD mind struggles with this considerably. It is learnable but requires specific instruction over a period of time by a skilled coach.

For the ASD adult, there is no generic image of an airport or what is expected in the airport situation. For some clients, there might be if they travel often, but if travel is an infrequent occurrence, there may be little to no visual images to tap into before embarking on a trip. Therefore, anxiety sets in early for some ASD adults, and they become fearful and irritated easily when traveling. Uninformed neurotypicals make assumptions that the ASD adult has an irrational fear or is being purposely non-compliant, but this is only because they cannot experience what the ASD adult is going through in this type of situation. Imagine having a blindfold put over your eyes and a pair of earplugs placed in your ears, and you now have to trust someone to guide you through the airport and put you safely where you need to be while you have very little control or information to go on to verify that everything is going as it should. Then, an unexpected occurrence causes your guide to disappear momentarily, and you begin to panic because you've lost your sense of vision, hearing, and the only accommodation to help you navigate the situation. This experience is what some would label as a meltdown. I call it a very rational and understandable fear of the unknown.

The best way to avoid a meltdown is obvious — preparation! The key to preventing a meltdown is through thorough preparation in all novel situations. Going back to the travel example, let's say you're going on your very first vacation as an adult. This particular trip requires transportation to the airport, a flight, and transportation to the hotel at your final destination. There are six hours of flight travel time and two hours of taxi transportation time. The total travel time is approximately eight hours and with traffic and flight delays, a common occurrence, we must build in an additional 1-2 hours of buffer time. So we now have to plan for a 10 hour travel day dedicated to just the traveling aspect of going on your first vacation. We just calculated the time you must prepare yourself to commit to in order to make this journey a success. If pulling a 10 hour day is not something you feel you can handle at this point in your life, then a shorter trip may be more appropriate for your first experience with travel. If you choose to go ahead with this particular trip, we must now go through all the main aspects of travel you need to be ready for.

Let's say, for simplicity's sake, that your friend has planned this trip and you are just along for the ride. The only thing you need to do in preparation is pack your checked bag and carry-on properly by reviewing your airline requirements online and getting in the taxi cab when it arrives at your house at 6 a.m. It takes an hour to get to the airport and your flight departs at 9:30 a.m. That gives you a half hour buffer in case there is traffic. You then have 2 hours to get through airport security (the recommended amount of time you should reserve for this process, but check your airline for any changes to this recommendation). In this particular scenario, you have plenty of time to get to the security section of your travels.

When getting into your taxi cab on your way to the airport, it is important to know what airport you are going to and which terminal and airline you will be traveling with. That way, your taxi driver will drop you off at the correct location. Once you arrive at the airport, you take your luggage to the check-in counter inside the airport (there will be signs to guide you) for your airline. By checking the airline's website previously, you ensure that you have packed correctly and meet the weight and size limits for your luggage. You may go up to a counter to check your bag or go to an automated kiosk. Some airlines use a combination of both methods and it may change each time you go to the airport, so look for signs and don't be afraid to ask for help if you need it. Sometimes you may even be able to check your bag at the curb where the taxi dropped you off. Once your bags are checked and taken away, it is now time to go to the security line. This line is usually very long and takes time to work through. If you need to use the restroom before getting in this long line, now is the time to do so.

Once in the security line, you should have your passport ready and be prepared to answer questions about yourself and where you are traveling. A security officer approves you to go through and your carry-on luggage is scanned. You will also walk through a scanner, so it is important to remove any metal objects before entering. You may also be told to remove your jacket or shoes if that is a requirement for that particular security checkpoint. Be mindful of the signs and direction from the security officers. Additionally, sometimes there are random screenings that are more in-depth, such as a hand wipe to check for explosives or a pat down. It is imperative that you are aware and compliant during these security screenings. To argue with or make a social error in this situation can cause you delays. Another possibility is that your luggage may be flagged for additional screening. If so, you must patiently wait for the screener to come over and check your bag. Politeness, gratitude, and direct answers are important to get through this situation. Once you have your carry-on luggage back, you can now proceed to your assigned gate. Your assigned gate is indicated on your boarding pass, and there are signs all over the airport with any updates concerning your gate number, so make sure you read those signs frequently and listen to the announcements.

Airports can be loud and bustling. You may want to bring a pair of noise-canceling headphones to help drown out the sound while you wait for your flight. You may also want to dress in layers to help keep yourself warmer or cooler. This is also an excellent time to shop for food or entertainment while you are awaiting your flight. If you got through security quickly, you will have a bit of waiting time before your fight. If security took longer than usual, you may not have much time to catch your flight, so make sure you go directly to your gate first to scope out the situation and then roam around if you choose. This is a great time to use the restroom and nourish yourself before the next leg of your journey. I usually use this opportunity to eat something, check my phone, and do any last minute preparations before I am without internet and cellular data for a few hours.

Now it is time to board your plane. The airline usually calls boarding zones. Your zone is listed on your boarding pass. When your zone is called, you can proceed to the gate and wait in line for them to scan your boarding pass and allow you into the plane. This usually takes some time and patience. You will then proceed directly to your seat. Once at your seat, you can stow your bag in the overhead compartment or under the seat in front of you — if it fits. Be prepared if your bag is on the larger side because they may ask you to check that bag at the gate if it will not fit on the plane. If you are asked to check your carry-on bag, you will have to do so, and it is free. It is important to take your important documents and items out before you give up your bag because you will not have access to it again until you land and proceed off of the plane. I always recommend using a smaller carry-on and not the roller bag if you wish to keep your bag with you at all times. You are also allowed a small personal item so this can be a bag dedicated to your important items in case your carry-on needs to be checked. Finally, you can now be seated.

Once seated, you will be waiting until the plane is fully boarded. After everyone is on the plane, you may have to wait for the rest of the luggage to be loaded. There is also the possibility of waiting for the plane to be cleared to leave. Once cleared, the plane will drive to the runway. This process can also take some time. There may even be a line of planes waiting to take off one at a time. It is now your plane's turn to take off. The pilot makes announcements throughout this whole process, and before take-off, you will hear the instruction for the flight attendants to take their seats and buckle up. You will be required to buckle your seatbelt whenever you are seated on the plane for safety reasons. The plane will then take off and you will soar into the sky. One you reach a certain height, the captain will inform you that you can move freely about the cabin as long as there isn't any turbulence. Turbulence feels like hitting bumps on the road when you are in a car. Sometimes turbulence can be mild, and other times it can be much more extreme. At times, it can feel like small little drops, like you are on an amusement park ride. This does not happen very often because they do their best to make the flight as smooth as possible, but you do need to be prepared for this possibility.

What comes next is usually drinks and/or snacks that are served on a flight. Non-alcoholic beverages are often complimentary along with some small snack, such as peanuts or pretzels. More recently, snacks cost a bit of money, so if you are willing to spend that money, you can make a purchase. Many people buy their snacks in the airport because it is cheaper and they can enjoy them whenever they wish, rather than waiting for food and beverage service to begin. I personally bring a bottle of water and some candy to get me through a flight, and I may treat myself to a complimentary ginger ale when the flight attendants come around. Once food and beverage service concludes it is time to tidy up and collect the garbage. I like to get rid of as much as possible at this point so I do not have to find a garbage receptacle inside the airport. Eventually, depending on the length of your flight, it is then time for the plane to descend. Everyone buckles up again, puts their electronics away and puts their seats in the upright position as the plane approaches the airport. Landing varies depending on the captain and the conditions, but it usually feels like gliding over a speed bump at high speed and then gently landing and a strong braking sensation, similar to a sensation you may have felt in a car. Most of the time it is fairly smooth and some people even clap once everyone is safely back on the ground. When the plane has landed and comes to a complete stop at the terminal, you are able to unbuckle, grab your bags, and proceed off the plane. You may have to go through customs if you traveled internationally or you may go directly to baggage claim. Once at baggage claim, you will retrieve your checked luggage. They usually have signs indicating where your luggage will be. Once you have your bags, you can go outside of the airport to look for your taxi. If you do not have a taxi pre-arranged, you can frequently take your pick at the airport, use an app to hire one, or ask someone to help you find one. You then have another hour drive to your hotel in this scenario. There could be traffic or luggage delays so make sure you stay alert and understand that you are still in traveling mode until you get to your hotel, check in, and take a load off (in other words, relax!).

This is a very detailed example that neurotypicals may find to be way too much information. For many on the spectrum, this type of information can help them considerably when navigating novel situations. Some on the spectrum may even benefit from an even more thorough explanation of all these steps. I alter my instructions based on the individual's needs. What I want neurotypicals to understand is that this is a very rough example of what it may be like for an adult on the ASD spectrum who is struggling with new situations. It is my description based on a neurotypical standpoint based on what my clients described to me so that I can put it into terms the average person will understand. What I want the reader to take from this one example is that this scenario can be applied to many new experiences for the ASD adult, the next of which is transitioning out of high school to a novel environment: college and university.

The key to an ASD adult being successful in college is preparation. I have had many clients attempt college without being provided with the proper background on what to expect which resulted in many disasters that could have been avoided. The college experience is much more than just academic learning and it varies considerably from what was experienced in high school. There are different types of academic expectations and demands, fewer accommodations available as compared to high school, and new types of personal responsibilities, such as living independently, that were never before undertaken when a student was living at home. In addition, college is a less structured environment than high school, with almost complete freedom to come an go as you please. This can be daunting to someone who has relied very much on structure and clearly defined boundaries for the majority of his or her life. What's more, the new social aspects of college may include a roommate, a different system of finding and maintaining friendships, a new system of dating, the availability of clubs and organizations, and the pressure of deciding on a major and future career. Let's examine the college experience in more detail and how preparation will make this transition much easier than thrusting an unprepared student, ASD or otherwise, into such a new and compounded scenario.

Most students are geared towards college to polish their knowledge, grow into a responsible adult, and to pursue a career in a specialized field. The academics of college and university are more complex than high school, but the work load is much different. There isn't necessarily more work to do; rather, there is a different type of work to do. For instance, most colleges begin with having students take a diverse amount of courses to fulfill college requirements before they move on to declaring a major and focusing on that major's courses. The majority of college courses require strong writing abilities. So, even if a student is a very strong math or science student, he or she may still have to take a long list of courses that require them to excel in more socially complex subjects. The reverse is also true. Additionally, the only accommodations allowed in college or university are more time on tests, a quiet room to test in, and perhaps note taking assistance. No accommodations will be made in terms of adjusting the curriculum. Similarly, parent involvement is limited to the point of shock for both the student and the parent. The student must be prepared to advocate for him or her self and know how to ask for help when needed. This is important because for most courses, each student is given a syllabus with all of the assignments and readings due throughout the semester. The student is responsible for planning out their studies and structuring their time appropriately. The professors instruct and happily provide assistance when asked, but they will not go out of their way to remind or push a student to succeed in the way a high school teacher might. They help those who want to be helped. Thus, as compared to high school, college course work is not necessarily more extensive, it simply requires the individual to structure and complete the work with little to no assistance.

When you are accustomed to an environment that was automatically structured for you, it becomes daunting when you now need to understand how to create structure for yourself.

Where do you begin when attempting to create your own routines, schedules, and incentives to complete your responsibilities? Well, I always start with a calendar. Use your high school experience as a template by creating a time to wake up each morning that allows you enough time to get ready for your first class of the day. When I was in college, one semester I had to get to an 8 a.m. class two days a week and 10 a.m. classes the other days. So my schedule on 2 of the days was different from my schedule on the remainder of the days of the week. Back then, I used a planner to create my schedule, but we have many more tools at our disposal today such as online calendars or apps that will help us get the job done. Once you have a schedule completed, you now need to follow and maintain that schedule on a regular basis. This is where establishing your routine comes in. It is imperative that you check and update that schedule each morning and evening so that you have an idea of how your day went and will go tomorrow. Every day should be as similar as possible so that you can get into a routine and schedule following groove. Lastly, now that you have an established routine, you also have to make sure you are completing your assignments and tasks on your own because college professors do not get on you to complete your work the way a high school teacher and/or your parents would. It is important for you to remember to do everything that is expected of you and to be able to live up to all of your responsibilities with little to no outside influences. You need to advocate for yourself. So, for instance, if you miss an assignment in high school, you may get a reminder from your teacher to complete the assignment. A college professor usually will not say a word. If you simply forgot, then you are not following a routine and schedule. If you were stuck and needed extra help with the assignment, it is your responsibility to arrange to meet up with your professor or other students to get assistance in understanding the material. Self-advocating is key because college and university life is all about your ability to ask for help when you need it. As long as you can do that, your chances of college success is great.

Moreover, for most students, this is the first time they experience complete freedom and independence if they are living on campus.Not only is the academic structure from high school disrupted, the home life structure is also abandoned when a student is now living on campus independently. Many clients struggle with getting themselves up in the morning, eating properly, getting to class and other appointments on time and independently, taking care of hygiene and their personal space, respecting their roommates space and privacy, and asking for help when they are struggling. It can be daunting to see other students navigating this complex social and academic arrangement with ease while the ASD student is struggling considerably. Many clients are afraid to ask for help or cannot see how it could be beneficial to their success. Others are so surprised by how much they need to do for themselves on top of achieving academically that they simply shut down. Then, unless the client has been given a single bedroom as an accommodation, learning to live with a roommate can be one of the most stressful and difficult social situations to navigate while at college. The level of intimacy required while simultaneously respecting the boundaries and privacy of a roommate is well beyond many of my client's capabilities without prior experience or instruction. Again, this is not true of every student with ASD because many have wonderful and long lasting relationships with their college roommates. Still, it is a common problem for many ASD adults that confounds the additional social struggles in the college environment.

There can be many scenarios here of what life was like before living on campus with a roommate. For instance, you may have been an only child who was always used to having your own space. Or perhaps you had siblings and were understanding of their very specific needs while your college roommate is completely different. Perhaps you disturb your roommate when he is trying to do work or the opposite is true. It can be very complicated to get along with a new person and even more distressing to also live with them. The key here is to communicate with your roommate on your needs and also to be open to and understanding of his or her needs. The schedule you made earlier may also need to take into account your roommate's schedule. Perhaps the two of you can come up with some dorm room rules that you both are expected to follow to keep things peaceful between the two of you. A room schedule on a white board or your phones can allow the two of you to divide up study and recreational time so that neither of you disturbs the other. The most important thing when dealing with a roommate is communication and being capable of regimenting yourself so that the two of you can keep the peace. At times, this can be very difficult, and on occasion, roommates do not work out. You can ask to be transferred and some schools allow ASD adults to have an accommodation where they get a single room instead of a shared room. All are acceptable solutions. Just remember to always seek out a solution. Do not suffer and do not allow a poor situation to fester when there is no need to allow that to happen. Although not always perfect, there is always a solution.

Furthermore, all of the above issues do not yet consider the additional social expectations of finding, making, and maintaining friendships in all of the various social situations of the college backdrop. From dorms to dining halls to classes and clubs, navigating all of these various social situations can be daunting for someone on the spectrum. In class, students have a very different way of communicating and interacting as compared to the dorm room or dining hall. The classroom in college also varies considerably from the high school classroom. Classes may have 10 to 500 students, depending on the course. In high school, there are really only 2-3 environments to navigate: the classroom, the lunch room, and physical education courses. In college there are many more various environments to master. Even some professors treat their students more like colleagues than as subordinates in class. This can vary from class to class and may be confusing for someone on the spectrum who has difficulty shifting from what is appropriate in one situation to what is appropriate in another. Likewise, the concept of authority is complicated for many of my clients. Shifting roles so often becomes confusing and anxiety producing. This is why many ASD adults get in trouble with the law. They fail to understand the complex rules of authority and when those rules change. The point in all of this is that college is a considerably more socially diverse experience that requires extensive preparation to ensure success for an ASD student with a history of social struggles.

How does one prepare for the social diversity of a college or university environment? Back in my high school years, I went to a private catholic institution that was predominantly filled with students from a white christian background who had enough money to pay for a private education. When I went off to college, I was suddenly surrounded by people of all cultures, religions (or lack of religions), beliefs, socioeconomic statuses and agendas. For many, especially those on the spectrum, this can be a culture shock. I thought it was amazing. In my experience, it felt like everyone was so different that we had that in common. It was so much easier for me to make friends in this type of environment. Embrace social diversity by remembering that everyone is in the same boat and on equal ground in college. I have found that in college, people are much more willing to be your friend because they, too, feel lost and thrust into a new and strangely diverse world. It is a great opportunity to expand your social circles and to learn more about a wide variety of people. Utilize the first level of friendship small talk phase skills you learned earlier and get involved straight away with attempting to make friends. Do not allow this task to wait until later in the semester when most social groups have already formed. Getting in early allows you to solidify your social standing from the very beginning of the semester.

Lastly, the choice of academic major and possible career paths can be extensive, and it may be difficult for someone on the spectrum to envision what each of these career paths may look like for the future. Most colleges or universities have a thick catalog of majors. With each of those majors come extensive lists of possible jobs and careers that can be pursued with that major. The decisions are daunting for any student, particularly those on the ASD spectrum. So much needs to be considered when making these decisions. Where does the student's talent lie? Is the coursework feasible for the student to complete successfully? Will the student be able to apply the academic achievement to real world job duties? Will the job or career environment be suited to this individual's needs and abilities, strengths and weaknesses? Is this choice of career realistic in terms of future prosperity and success? I have had, on multiple occasions, clients and their parents come to me with the desire, for example, to become a video game designer because of their love of video games. The love of video games alone does not necessarily mean you will excel at designing them. It is a great idea, but it is only viable if there is a talent to work through all of the college requirement courses, courses of game design, if they are skilled enough to compete with others pursuing the field, as well as understand all the complexities both social and technical of working at a game design company in the future. Some of my clients have done all of this, but for others, it was not a realistic path.

Many who go to college have no clue what they will do with the rest of their lives. The mentality these days is go to university so that you can prepare for a career in a specific field. The majority of college students today do not end up in their field of study. At the conclusion of college, many end up in an entry-level position in order to gain experience before landing a high-level job. I feel it is extremely beneficial to have realistic career expectations during your college career and upon graduation. Unless you excel academically and have a good solid resume of both academic and internship experience, it is highly unlikely you will dive right into your dream job or career. Of course, there are exceptions to this rule. I have a highly intelligent cousin who excelled in engineering and had a summer internship that led to permanent employment at a world renowned financial institution upon graduation. This is not the norm! He was exceptional and excelled in both intellectual and social areas and still does to this day. He has many gifts. Then, take me for example. I am average to slightly above average in intelligence and social understanding. Right out of college, I was able to obtain an entry-level position at a company that had nothing to do with what I wanted to do with the rest of my life. I ended up quitting and going back to graduate school so that I could obtain the education I needed to at least gain a position my field. The majority of people who complete university go on to an entry-level position to gain work history and experience. After 1-2 years, that work experience combined with your academic knowledge can land you a high-level position. Excelling and growing in that higher position will then lead to other opportunities, either within that company or elsewhere. You will also have the chance to better yourself with further education or certifications and other opportunities to continually develop valuable skills. Some go off to start their own companies or develop a completely new passion. Just remember that your expectations should be high as long as they are realistic to your level of ability. Make sure you are developing your abilities to their fullest potential so that you have the greatest chances of success when you go out into the career realm. Real success is nothing more than being content with your career and having everything you need to survive. Again, extensive preparation for all aspects of college — including the social experience, the academic path and discovering a realistic career direction — are essential in achieving true college or university success. I will discuss how life coaching, specifically for ASD adults, can assist substantially in this area in the second part of this book. We now can move on to the next transition into the adult world: beginning a job and establishing a career.

CHAPTER 3

Finding a Job and Establishing a Career

Once college has been completed, we are again transitioning into a new and even larger environment with a whole new set of circumstances, expectations, and requirements. High school was a contained environment where there were boundaries and limited but clear expectations. Similarly, college was an environment with clear expectations (completing a degree), but it was a much more vast experience with fewer boundaries and wider ranging possibilities. Once college is completed, the job and career paths one can choose are virtually limitless. For someone on the ASD spectrum, having almost unlimited options can be quite daunting. Where does one even begin when entering this very new and often uncharted territory? The majority of clients I have worked with have never had a job before or during their college years. Most of the time, they focused 100% on their studies with little to no preparation for what is to come. The shift to a job and career mentality can be quite shocking when the focus of the previous 4 years was on completing a college degree. Furthermore, while college is tremendously less structured than high school, there is still some order in the form of syllabi outlining what is expected in class and where you are required to be at certain times throughout the day. Not many colleges or universities offer instruction on how to pursue a career in a step-by-step fashion after graduation. What I will do here is attempt to outline the practical steps involved in pursuing a career once college has been completed. This outline can be helpful to any college graduate but most notably for our students on the spectrum.

The first step in transitioning into the job world is to have some idea of what type of job or career you are interested in exploring further. Having a degree does not automatically mean you have a specific career in mind. In fact, most college graduates end up in a field they didn't intend to pursue initially but stumbled upon later. I often give examples from my own life to my clients in an attempt to normalize that plans are not set in stone. Real-life shifts and takes various turns. For instance, in my own college career, I initially intended to get into computer science. I wanted to become a programmer. I quickly learned that I was not up to the mathematical challenge ahead. Sadly, I learned that it was not a realistic path for me to take. I was crushed and had to figure out a new path. As a result, I remember taking the big book of college majors and reading through all of them one-by-one until I found one that made the most sense to me: psychology. I followed that path and can still remember sitting in my professor's office one afternoon and imagining having a similar office in the future. To my surprise, once I graduated, I had short stints in jobs that had nothing to do with my major field of study. Newly motivated, I then went on to pursue a Master's degree so that I could be qualified to work as a therapist in a specialized field. Even then, my plans didn't pan out exactly as I had envisioned them. I was frustrated with the lack of education, training, and information on ASD, and that frustration turned into a passion to start my own company to better work with this population of people. I stumbled upon my path. In fact, most college graduates end up in a field they didn't intend to pursue but fell into later. Of course, some students know exactly what kind of career they will seek out after college, but the majority of students haven't nailed down a career path until well after graduation, often years later. For that majority who may be struggling with the next steps after college, let's examine a step-by-step approach to make that job and future career search a bit easier to envision.

One of the first questions I ask a college graduate is whether or not they have a resume and cover letter. The initial step in a job search is to have your qualifications on paper as well as a standard letter expressing your interest in a job opportunity. Not only is a resume a great way to show potential employers your training, experience, and skills, it also shows the applicant what they have accomplished and where they may like to head in the future. A basic resume has the applicant's personal information, an objective or statement of intent, work experience, education, skills, special achievements, and references. If you have most of these basic categories, your resume is already shaping up to be an effective tool in your job search. In addition to a resume, it is vital to have a cover letter. Often clients feel the resume is more than enough to outline their skills, but a cover letter makes the application more personal and is a great way to make that initial social connection with a potential employer to move them to call you in for an interview. Without the cover letter, you are just another number in the pile of resumes on the table or in an email inbox. A basic cover letter comprises of the applicant's personal information, the address and information of the employer, a greeting, and three paragraphs of information. The first paragraph is an introduction stating why you are writing, the position you are interested in, and why you are a good fit for that position. The second paragraph refers to your resume and supports why you feel you would be a good fit for the company or organization. The final paragraph of the cover letter should reiterate interest in the position, request a meeting to discuss the job opportunity further, and express appreciation to the potential employer for their time and consideration. Finally, the cover letter should be signed and the resume enclosure should be indicated. Combined with a resume, the cover letter is a powerful tool to make that very important social connection with a potential employer before you ever verbally speak to them or make that initial physical contact with a handshake. These tools will be what sells you for that initial interview.

The most difficult part of making a resume and cover letter is getting started. Usually, when a client groans over the seemingly enormous task of creating a resume from scratch, I start them off with a template. You do not need a coach for this because you can look up resume templates online or use your word processing software's built-in templates. I have also included a simple sample resume and cover letter at the end of this book in the appendix. Once you have a template, or a place to start, everything else is fairly simple to fill in. Now, if that task is truly too difficult for you, do not fear. There are coaches, professional resume writers, parents, teachers, and other people in your network who will be more than willing to help you as long as you reach out and ask for that help if you need it. The main idea and theme of this book is continually taking some sort of action to move forward. Do not allow yourself to remain stuck. If you remain stuck, everyone else around you continues to advance. So when you stay the same, you inadvertently fall further and further behind your peers because they are continually moving forward. The longer you let this go, the more difficult it becomes to catch up. Seek out answers when you are at an impasse and you shall receive many possible solutions to help keep you moving in the right direction.

Indeed, the job interview is something that makes many people anxious, especially those on the spectrum who already struggle with social interaction. I have found that extensive job interview preparation can help considerably. If you know what to expect, you are much more likely to succeed than if you are thrust into an unfamiliar situation. This is a common theme you will find throughout this book. Preparation is always the key to success. In session, I often do mock interviews with clients and go over all of the standard interview questions. I always throw in some unexpected questions so that my clients are prepared for almost anything. In addition, we discuss at length when to elaborate on a question and when to withhold too much information. This can be a very tricky thing to teach. It is difficult for many of my clients to understand when a piece of information is legitimately private or when it is essential to a successful interview. The best way to teach these complicated concepts is to practice as much as possible with various scenarios and examples so that the client has a repertoire of information to pull from during the actual interview.

Now, before an interview can take place, we need to actually search out job postings, apply for internships and/or utilize career services either at our alma mater or in our local community. There are countless websites, apps and good old fashioned paper postings of potential jobs to navigate through. Similarly, there are many tools out there to help narrow down the search by taking into account the client's interests, skills, strengths and weaknesses. The right kind of job should have an environment best suited to the individual client, be employment the client can complete at their own pace, and be a duty that they can be passionate about and/or gain some sort of personal reward from performing. For example, a job in retail involves interacting with a large number of demanding customers in a fast paced environment. Many initial jobs are retail positions because they require little experience and are easily found due to the high demand and turn over rate in the business. This does not mean it will be a proper first job for an adult on the spectrum. We need to take into consideration much more than just the capability of performing the specified job duties and take a closer look at how the surroundings will affect job performance in the individual. I have found great success for clients who start off in small offices doing basic office computer or paperwork. The environment is more intimate, the social interaction is minimized but not nonexistent, and this type of job can lead to more advanced positions in the future. It is imperative to note that this is not appropriate for every client. We must take the individual's needs, wants, desires, skills, strengths and weaknesses into account when deciding the appropriate job to apply for. We should not just accept any job.

The reason for this is that the appropriate work environment is different for each individual. What is very appropriate for one person will be a nightmare for another. What are the appropriate surroundings for you? Will you succeed in the retail environment if you do not like to interact with people or work in a fast paced environment? Most likely not. Perhaps a quieter and slower paced position is best for you. I had a client who had a terrible experience working at a huge retail store where she was constantly in demand, but she flourished in a small bistro environment where she needed to take care of one or two customers at a time. We should not waste time on positions that will overwhelm us; rather, we should seek out positions where we know the environment is appropriate to our strengths and takes into account our weaknesses. The pace of the work is also an important factor in deciding which jobs to apply for. For instance, if you struggle with intensive computer work where frequent reports are needed throughout the day, then a fast-paced office environment that expects a high level of output is going to be a very difficult challenge. However, if you find a position where you can take your time with reports or computer tasks that are not in immediate demand, you may do much better. A good example of a slower paced office environment may be in a small business that does a few jobs or handles a few accounts, rather than a large company that handles hundreds of clients a day. These differences in company size and work output demand make a huge difference in what is expected in terms of work pace. Choose wisely when applying to jobs that may be too quickly paced for your abilities. Lastly, while initially at the entry-level we are looking to obtain a job that will provide us with work experience, we still want to make sure that position is rewarding to the individual at some level. We also want that job to be able to expand or at least lead us to an even more rewarding position in the future. For example, if you wish to get into accounting, it may not be appropriate to start off as a receptionist. You want to start off in a job that is related to and where you will have opportunities to do some accounting. A clerk is a lower level accounting position that will help give you the entry-level experience you need to get you to your goal of becoming an accountant. That will be much more rewarding than a receptionist position that requires skills you do not necessarily have, want, or need to pursue your accounting career. Generalize this example to whatever it may be that you wish to attain as a career in the future. Overall, if we want to succeed, we must take the time to find the appropriate surroundings, ideal work pace, and rewarding nature of a job opportunity if we expect to grow that experience into a lasting career. If all of these criteria are met, the chances of obtaining and succeeding at the future job increase exponentially.

Moving back to the job interview, this initial impression is what makes or breaks the job opportunity. Many on the spectrum struggle with first impressions. The job interview is the ultimate situation where first impressions are most important. There are rarely second chances when it comes to an interview, whereas in most other social aspects of life, there is more leeway to correct social mistakes. The amount of pressure and anxiety that can stem from knowing how important this moment is can be overwhelming for many people, not just those on the ASD spectrum. I mentioned earlier that preparation is key to nailing a job interview. In order to be adequately prepared for this type of social process, one must be well versed in standard interview questions, had practice answering those questions completely and effectively, been provided with feedback and professional advice on one's interviewing skills, and be well informed on each company's basic information as well as what is expected and sought after in a potential hire. It is impossible to sell yourself to a potential employer if you are not ready to sell your abilities, prove your potential value to the company, and display your knowledge and desire to be part of that team.

So how can you succeed at a job interview? Well, let us define job interview success. Obtaining the job is not the only indicator of success here. You could absolutely nail a job interview to the best of your ability and impress at a high-level and still not get the job. There is always the possibility that there will be a better fit for that position, no matter how well you do. So, job rejections should not be discouraging or taken as the sole indicator of job interview success or failure. We must make sure we hit all of the key job interview points: 1. Come off as likable and easy to interact with in the interview with all interviewers. 2. Be knowledgeable about yourself, your skills, and the company you are interviewing for. 3. Be prepared to have a back and forth dialogue with the interviewer that shows you have mastered reciprocal conversation. 4. Exude confidence, not arrogance, by asking questions pertinent to both the job expectations and company life. All this requires is extensive preparation, just as if you were studying for and practicing for a test or oral presentation. You are presenting yourself. If you struggle with knowing how to present yourself and are not getting enough education on your own through books or the internet, then it would be prudent to get a job coach or knowledgeable associate to assist in this preparation, just as you would seek out tutoring for an academic struggle. A life coach, or more specifically a job coach could certainly prepare you for these challenging interview experiences. Therefore, the job interview is not simply about your written out skills on a resume. It is about making a meaningful and purposeful connection with the person interviewing you. If you can connect with that person on a socially professional level consistently, you will have mastered the job interview process.

Frequently, very talented clients get highly discouraged when they go on a job interview, seemingly do well, and then do not get any feedback or offers. For many on the spectrum, self-confidence is often a struggle. Not getting an offer can feel like rejection and a failure. The reality is that we are not perfect and there is always someone more skilled than we are who may have also gone on that job interview. For instance, I consider myself a highly skilled life coach. However, I also realize that there are numerous people in this world who are better and more knowledgeable than I am in this field. This does not make me feel bad about myself. Instead, I realize that I can hold my own, and as long as I do the best that I can with the talent I have and the hard work I put into everything I set my mind to, I am doing well. Sometimes I get chosen to work with a client and other times another professional is a better fit. It is the same concept when going on a job interview. You may be amazingly talented and hard working, but there simply might be a better fit for that company. It is important to see that this is not a personal rejection but rather a decision by that company to go in another direction. The point of this example is that not all rejection is equal. As long as we don't give up our job search and work through rejections in a healthy manner, which are a normal part of all aspects of life, we will eventually find the right place of employment. I had to go as far as to create my own place of employment, and that is acceptable too!

Likewise, many on the autism spectrum struggle with any type of rejection. As you logically know, rejection is part of life. Being on the losing end is a lesson we are supposed to learn early in life. Today, that is a bit difficult, especially when we are used to getting participation trophies and taught to avoid failure or not admit to defeat. The reality is that we all get rejected, no matter how good we are at anything. Most people lose out on a potential job opportunity. The most intelligent, successful people today can tell you stories of how they were rejected in the past. Think about some of the billionaires of the world today who tell their early stories of rejection and defeat. Rejection is part of how we learn and grow and find the right opportunities in life, whether that be in a relationship or our careers. How does one deal with rejection when we are already down on ourselves after years of struggle? Well, the best thing to do is understand the rejection logically. When you go on a job interview, you are most likely not the only candidate. So right off the bat, you have competition. This competition is beyond your control. Therefore, you must go into that job interview as prepared as possible. You do not know the skill level or preparation level of your competition. Therefore, you must do the best you possibly can. If your skills are not as sharp as or better than the competition, you will not get the position. That does not mean you failed. That means this particular position was a better fit for someone else. Logically, that makes sense. Emotionally, it sucks. It does not feel good to know that someone else is better than us. However, one day, if you keep at it, prepare thoroughly, and find the right fit for you and a company, you will become the next person to get an opportunity to shine in a position that will lead you towards your future career. Others will then have to face the rejection and move on to something else. The best thing you can do when faced with rejection is to accept it, process the emotions that come along with it, and then pick yourself up and move on to the next opportunity. You only truly fail if you stop trying. A high percentage of people on the spectrum are unemployed, yet 100% of those individuals are employable. You are employable, you are valuable, and when you find and take the right opportunity you will flourish. The key is to stay persistent, make realistic goals to achieve ,and continually work to improve your skills and abilities. For example, a doctor doesn't stop learning all of the latest research once he becomes a doctor. If he stopped continually working on his skills and abilities, he would quickly and miserably fail as a doctor in an ever-changing field. The same applies to all of us. We never achieve absolute knowledge or ability. We keep growing and as long as we do, we will eventually discover and obtain suitable employment. On average, it takes approximately 3 months to find a job for a new client who sets that as one of his or her goals in the coaching session.

Now, I do not simply stop seeing a client once they accomplish the goal of finding a job. We must work together during this critical time to make sure that job is maintained successfully over the course of the next 3 months and beyond. It is one task to get a job and another task all together to keep that job. In order to effectively secure your place in a new position, a client must understand the hierarchy of authority at the organization, follow instructions completely, perform tasks and duties in a timely manner, have a good relationship with the boss, interact appropriately with the other employees and customers, as well as obey all the rules and expectations of that company as a whole. I once had a client who worked at a wine store. This client was full of knowledge and could tell you everything you wanted to know about a wine's vintage, the grapes used, the history of the vineyard, the tastes and textures of the wine and more. He ended up drawing customer's in and selling highly expensive bottles of wine as if it were second nature to him. One day, his boss pulled him aside and reprimanded him for selling small amounts of really expensive wine that he would now have to restock. He proceeded to ask my client to stop wasting time selling expensive bottles and instead to push the cheaper varieties of wine since that was what made the store the most money. My client could not understand why he was being told to stop being knowledgeable and charming and successfully making sales, so he disregarded his employer's advice. One month later, he was fired. Needless to say, he was devastated and shocked. He could not comprehend that while he was demonstrating great knowledge, talent, and ability, he was not displaying respect for authority, and the inability to follow directions had damaged his relationship with his boss in the process. So you can see that maintaining employment is just as important as finding that job opportunity. Finding the job opportunity is where demonstrating great knowledge, talent, and ability will solidify being hired, while maintaining that job depends on all of that as well as understanding complicated social constructs. We, as coaches, need to be there to support our clients during that critical period of time.

So how do you maintain a job on your own? In order to maintain a job, you must actively listen and follow directions from your superiors. You must also complete all of the duties in your job description to their fullest. It is also essential to socialize with the other employees successfully so that team work flows and that there is a general feeling of understanding and likability between you and your co-workers. Teamwork is another important aspect of being able to maintain employment. If you can communicate and effectively collaborate with your peers, you will be accepted and respected. Another important thing is to be able to follow instructions and ask for clarification when you are uncertain of how to proceed. Most employers want their employees to be able to work independently without much supervision, so making sure you ask all of your questions and take notes in order to avoid repetitive instruction is imperative. Finally, the most important thing is to master the concept of knowing when to be a leader and when to be a follower. Many on the spectrum mistake being a follower as a bad thing while being a leader is a good thing. This is a great example of not seeing the grey area. There are times when it is more appropriate and helpful to be a follower and times when taking the lead and guiding others is the best choice. Sometimes we are assigned leadership and must do our best to fill that role successfully. Other times, we are going to be much more effective as a follower for the greater good of the project, assignment, or the company as a whole. A good example of this is the wine store scenario I described earlier. That client could have been very successful if he relinquished his self-assigned leadership role of selling expensive wines and became a follower to his superior's instructions. He would have obtained employment, maintained employment and would have had a solid employment history to advance in his career, and possibly one day, he would have become the leader.

So, in terms of career, once we know a job is stable and employment is solidified, we can discuss career advancement. A good rule of thumb is to spend about a year at a company learning the ropes and building your reputation before seeking out advancement. It can be difficult these days because many companies are not offering raises or growth opportunities as much as they used to. That is why you must be strategic when asking for a raise or a promotion. In terms of a raise, it is important to make sure your work is impeccable, you complete all work that is expected of you, and that you go above and beyond in your work to justify further compensation. It's necessary to document this extra work so that you can show evidence as to why you deserve more money going forward. If you are doing work that is outside of the realm of your initial position with the company and that work is more advanced, you can start collecting evidence to justify a promotion. Before asking for a promotion, it is also a good idea to check out some other job opportunities and possibly even get a new job offer to present to your current employer as leverage. If they won't promote or compensate you accordingly, you would have to take the new position to continue to further your career. This is often a big enough motivator to get your current employer to realize your worth and give you the recognition that you deserve. In terms of proper advancement and reaching your career goals, I like to use my husband as an example when talking about career growth because he masterfully rose up the ranks throughout his career in a very orderly and logical manner. Initially, he worked at a small drug store near his home at just above minimum wage. Once he graduated college, it was time for him to advance to a career better suited to his education and abilities. He obtained an accounting clerk III position after utilizing a temp agency to help him find an open position. Once at that company, he learned the ropes, and as more and more employees got laid off or left the company, he continued to grow and advance up the ranks. His hard work and dedication went recognized while other employees stayed in the same place. He surpassed every other employee over the course of a decade. Eventually, he became the assistant controller. That lead to controller, and years down the line, he proved himself valuable enough by temporarily leaving the company for a higher paying position, later to be lured back to become the chief financial officer of that company. When, due to circumstances beyond his control, that company went under, he decided to start his own business and rose to the very top of the ranks as owner and chief executive officer. The admiration and pride I feel for my husband is beyond words. He inspired me to start my own company and make a difference in the world by following my passion and using my abilities to the fullest. I try to share that lesson with all of my clients because I know if we can do it, they can do it too.

CHAPTER 4

Independent Living and Relationships

There is so much more to life than holding down a job. In fact, not all jobs provide a living wage. A living wage would be a salary that allows for an individual to pay for food, clothing, living necessities, monthly bills and rent/mortgage. Some fun and entertainment should be included in these calculations simply because recreation is a need, perhaps not a bare minimum need, but some sort of fun is necessary for a good quality of life. Now, in order to figure out what your living wage is, creating a budget can help visualize it and be used as a tool to stick to that budget over time in order to prove you can financially survive on that wage. First and foremost, your budget needs to include monthly rent or mortgage payments. If you cannot afford this payment, living independently is going to be extremely difficult. Remember, living independently does not always have to mean living alone. It is perfectly acceptable to have a roommate or significant other that you split rent with in order for it to be affordable. If you do not want a roommate, then finding ways to make more money or find less expensive accommodations is a must. Besides rent, one must make sure all of the necessities to survival are met. This includes budgeting for food. There are a variety of ways to make your food budget affordable. Obviously, the most cost effective way to obtain food is by purchasing it at the grocery store and cooking it at home. If you are the type of person who prefers to buy pre-made food or go to restaurants exclusively, you will need to adjust your budget accordingly.

In addition to food, transportation is another big and necessary expense. This includes maintaining a car, gas, and insurance, or paying for some type of public transportation, which is also completely acceptable. If your salary or income allows for you to easily pay for food, transportation, and rent, you are well on your way to having a living wage. However, there are still more expenses that need to be taken into account. For instance, you will need renters/home owner's insurance coverage, gas, electric, sewer/water, clothing, toiletries, health insurance coverage, and a buffer of funds in case of emergency. Other bills that are likely but not mandatory are cell phone, internet, cable, entertainment, luxury items, home maintenance and much more. The ability to pay for the bare minimum and get by in life by following your budget is when you know you have obtained an adequate living wage and can financially live independently. It is important to note that living independently is not just the ability to financially pay for things but to also be able to manage day-to-day living. You must ask yourself if you can get up for work each morning and successfully maintain employment for the long-term. Notably, bills must be paid each month and on time. Additionally, personal hygiene, home cleanliness and maintenance must occur regularly. It is one thing to have enough money to pay for your car breaking down and another to actually arrange for and take it to be repaired. Is following a personal calendar or schedule independently a doable venture? If so, you are fully capable of independent living. It is important to note that I encourage clients to live independently even if they are struggling to make ends meet, but it is ideal to be able to afford everything with a savings account continually growing over time. I promote and assist all of my clients in budgeting for savings, investments, and retirement. There is a sample monthly budget in the appendix of this book. Utilize it by filling in your expenses and adjust it according to your individual needs. Your goal is to be able to afford all of your needs and a few wants on your monthly income. There is always a way to adjust to make those numbers work. If you struggle, then it would be prudent to seek out a life coach or a professional who specializes in budgeting. You are then well on your way towards understanding how to become financially independent.

Mastering independent living while single is one of the most challenging tasks we face as adults. What complicates things further is when you add a potential relationship to the mix. Dating is both a time and financial commitment. When the time comes to start dating, it must be worked into the budget and the daily/weekly/monthly routine. We will get into the social aspects of dating in a later chapter. For now, we will discuss how living independently is affected by dating, cohabitation, marriage, and later life demands. Let's start with dating. When we have employment, the workplace is sometimes one arena where we tend to meet potential partners. It is our main social outlet and place we spend the majority of our day. We see the same people on a daily basis and relationships often stem from that proximity in time and space. Sometimes, meeting a romantic interest at work is perfectly acceptable, and other times, it is frowned upon and can lead to employment complications. Still, many people meet at work and it is quite possible you as the reader have met or will meet someone in that environment. Other places to potentially meet a romantic interest are gyms, churches, schools or colleges, social events, and in the times of social media: online. Once we meet someone we have an interest in and that person feels the same way, dating can begin. We will discuss the nuances of dating in another chapter. For now, we will focus on how dating affects independent living. In order to date someone, we must make room in our lives or schedule in order to spend time with that person. We spend time with people in order to get to know them and find out if they are relationship material. It is imperative to be able to balance and adjust so that we can add that person into our lives. We also need to adapt if that relationship ends and we are left with extra time to fill with that person is no longer around. If a relationship builds and over time both people want to combine lives through cohabitation or marriage, a whole new set of time commitments come into play as well as making daily life commitment changes. There will be new expectations put upon you and new results.

How does one adjust to dating commitments? I had a client who had a very rigid routine. He would get up every morning and play on his cell phone for about an hour while still in bed. After that period of relaxation, he would then go on to make breakfast, shower, get dressed, and go off to work. After work, he would come home, make dinner, and play video games before bed. His routine was simple but satisfying. Still, he desperately wanted a romantic relationship. Once he found that relationship, it was wonderful. He now had someone to spend time with and talk to and to enjoy all of the romantic perks he always dreamed about. Almost immediately, his routine was thrown off. He was spending time late at night texting with his girlfriend and he would wake up later and later in the mornings before work. This cut into his morning cell phone relaxation time. He would end up getting to work a bit agitated and feeling rushed. Also, spending time with his girlfriend after work caused him to miss out on his valuable video game time, causing him to miss out on the way he typically relaxed after a long day. This was quite distressing because he thought having a relationship meant having it all. Soon he realized that he couldn't maintain the exact same routine or schedule without adjusting to the demands of his new relationship. Together, we worked on ways he could adjust his routine without cutting any activities out. Instead, we worked on changing the timing of his routines to accommodate the new relationship. This included putting some time limits on the relationship itself. Now, he could have the time he needed in order to relax before and after work so that he could continue to be an effective employee. This also allowed him to have more energy and focus on the relationship itself so that it could develop into something long lasting.

Marriage between two people is one of the biggest, if not the biggest, commitment we make in life. It is a statement of love and dedication to each other for all the world to see. With it comes a whole new set of responsibilities and expectations that go beyond living independently as an individual. For instance, once married, you become legally responsible for the other person's health, finances, companionship, and general well-being. The reverse is true for yourself. Marriage is a contract between two people stating that you dedicate yourself to each other in all of these realms. This is why it is imperative that you do not rush into marriage but instead discuss and plan it at length before making that commitment. I typically advise waiting two years before getting engaged because that is approximately how long it take to truly get to know someone. Now, while each individual's needs still remain important, marriage becomes a time where two people must work together and communicate as a unit in order for that marriage to be successful and lasting. During the dating phase and engagement period, which typically lasts a year or so, it is wise to practice communicating and functioning as one. This is easier said than done and remains of of the most difficult life events to master, not just for an ASD adult.

How do we take two separate people with differing needs, wants, and desires and have them function both independently and as a unit? The key is, of course, communication. When we bring another person into our life, we must adjust that life. Our partner must adjust his or her life as well. It is not so much of a sacrifice as it is a combining or leveling up. So where there are some sacrifices that have to be made when you add someone into your life, there are also tremendous bonuses. For instance, while you may lose some personal time during the day in order to spend it with your significant other, you also gain time by perhaps sharing household responsibilities. Likewise, you may lose reading time while eating dinner but gain a partner to have an engaging conversation with at during that time. It all balances out over time, as long as the two people in the relationship are able to communicate and negotiate their time together. It is important in relationships to be able to clearly communicate your needs, wants, desires, and expectations. Then you need to be able to negotiate with each other so that the two of you can come up with a combined life plan that satisfies everyone. This is how we function as a unit. If two people are on the same page about how to structure the day, it becomes much easier to structure the trajectory of your lives in terms of career, marriage, parenthood, and everything that comes both in-between and after.

After marriage, many, though not all, decide to start a family. The reader by now can see that mastering independent living is leading towards being capable of living a much more social experience as the marriage grows into becoming a family unit. Obviously, parenthood is a major life event. We all start off learning how to take care of ourselves so that we may one day understand how to do the same for our family. The wants, needs, desires, and expectations the individual has in life now becomes confounded with the wants, needs, desires, and expectations of not only a significant other but also children who require a much higher degree of care than an adult spouse. The goal of every parent is to raise a healthy, happy human being who can one day grow up to achieve independence and continue the cycle of life anew. The most difficult aspect of being a parent for the ASD adult, besides financial pressures, is being able to put your own needs on the back burner in order for your child to be properly nurtured and grow. So back when we were learning to add a romantic partner to our lives, there was a lot of negotiation and communication. It was difficult to make some sacrifices, but there were also many bonuses to combining lives. Now, building a family by adding children is a whole other experience. We can only negotiate with children to a certain degree. When they are infants, it is very important that we are ready to sacrifice much more. A child is a helpless creature that requires the parents to temporarily put aside their own needs and wants so that the child can survive and thrive. That means that it might not be possible to have your video game time in the evenings if someone needs to feed and care for the baby at that time. That want has to be put aside in the critical infant stages so that the baby is fed and healthy. Sometimes both can be juggled, but it is the experience of many new parents that things will have to be sacrificed such as hobbies, relaxation, and quite often, the basic need of sleep. Still, this sacrifice is temporary and evolves over time. Children get older and become more self-sufficient as time goes on. Parents teach their children how to do more and more for themselves, and soon, parents gain back the time they sacrificed for their children. It is important to make the choice to have children after careful consideration. If you are willing to make these changes in order to start a family, it will still be difficult at times. However, most say that sacrifice is more than worth it when that helpless child becomes an adult and continues the cycle of life.

Eventually, children grow and the process continues through them. Still, your own life growth and journey continues on. We all get older and enter new phases of our lives. Our own parents begin to age and we may need to help take care of them as they lose their ability to function independently themselves. A new family social dynamic could form with either your own parents or your spouse's parents. You yourself may need to lean on your own children for assistance as time goes on. The importance of your family social unit becomes very clear around this stage of life. Additionally, not all marriages are destined to last, and divorce is a very real possibility at any stage after marriage and throughout this later life process due to a variety of potential life circumstances. Learning how to adjust to these possibilities is one of the greatest challenges as we grow older. The ultimate losses often, but not always, occur later in life. We may have to grieve the loss of parents, siblings, extended family members, and even our own spouse. Similarly, facing our own potential illnesses or death comes at this point as well. These are all just facts of life that we all have to face at some point as we age. Our own mortality is the ultimate culmination of our journey through socialization, independence, and interdependence. It can be beneficial to face these inevitabilities by being prepared. True, we can never be fully prepared for the ultimate tragedies of life, but we can do our best to make sure we build powerful social connections within and around our families for support so that all of the constant life transitions can be experienced to their fullest.

We have now come to the end of the first part of this book. The purpose of this section was to give the reader a thorough overview of living with ASD in adulthood and the expectations that come with being an adult. Most everything outlined here is usually not discussed in depth by neurotypicals but rather silently expected and achieved. Now we can delve into how life coaching can help adults on the ASD spectrum successfully navigate everything discussed previously as well as deal with more complexities that stem from these various areas and expectations of life. Life coaching is about teaching skills and providing tools the individual can use to successfully master and achieve in each phase of life. The majority of people learn these skills and have access to these tools more intuitively. Still, that does not mean someone with ASD is incapable of learning these skills and utilizing the correct tools. They simply need to be taught in a very individualized way based on that particular person's way of thinking and learning. We will now examine life coaching further and the potential role it plays in the ASD adult's future success.

PART II: FOR THE COACH

Life Coaching Adults on the ASD Spectrum

FOREWORD

Francesco Paladino, CCC

On April 1863, a fragmented statue was discovered by the amateur archaeologist, Charles Champoiseau. The statue was simply named the *Winged Victory of Samothrace,* because it had wings and had come from the Greek island of Samothrace. Yes, self explanatory to say the very least. Before you start to Google this to double-check if you already know about it, I am here to say that you do. "Victory" may not be as recognizable as *The Mona Lisa* or a silkscreened *Campbell* soup can, but she is still pretty well known. Even if you are the type of guy who goes to car shows and you watch *Duck Dynasty,* you might know it. Maybe. She has made appearances in cartoons, on t-shirts, parodies, and music videos. She is best identified as the marble lady with no arms or head. Sound more familiar? I thought so. She was decapitated during one of those "Clash of the Titans'" types of wars we heard about while half napping in high school. One group of men in togas got mad at another group of men in togas, and all the art had to suffer. If you take the togas out of this story, nothing has changed. The marble lady stands at nine feet tall with her wings extended behind her as if she was heading to a Vegas stage for the closing number. This was, of course, before some Hercules dude cut her head off. Actually, her original home was a perch above the stage in a Greek theatre. "Victory" has been reassembled in stages since her first discovery, using the debris from the original excavation to form more details on her body, constantly trying to make her better. She is seen as a victory, even though she may never have a head, a face, arms, or hands. None of that matters when you've had your massive wings since

190 BC.

Achieving victory is subjective. We change our careers to impress our parents. We change our careers because we think we will be richer or happier. And, of course, we change our careers for the good old fashioned reason called... survival. For me, my careers were always a personal transition into the next logical step. For any onlooker, my journey seems illogical, but for me, it made perfect sense. A chronological reinvention that was mapped out from one life changing graduation to the other. With my life, it was as if you read a recipe for breadmaking and the recipe called for *Elmer's Glue* and mint chocolate chip ice cream. No matter where life took me thus far, it made perfect sense. My career started as an actor in a commercial or two, some bit roles in movies, television, that led to *Screen Actors Guild* status. Then as a theatre actor, then stand-up comedian, and then a writer for other funny people and writing for television and theatre. While doing all of the above, I was a bartender and a motivational public speaker. Exhausting, right? Public speaking felt like stand-up at a *Ted Talk.* I was sent out to the crowd to "warm them up" with antidotes about being a father or about growing up a fat kid. All very inspiring stuff.

I was fortunate to bartend fancy private parties and corporate events. I got to avoid the dark smokey holes that leave you with a sad 13 bucks in tips on a Tuesday night. Bartending always seemed like an entertainment person's stereotypical requirement, but it certainly guaranteed a consistent way to make some dough. I must admit that my justification for filling glasses was much deeper. I needed to graduate to the next level. This was my bridge to something else. I wasn't sure what that "something else" was, but I just did it. I didn't know who I would meet or where I was going, but I trusted and believed it would be the right answer — the answer to a question that I didn't even ask. Even on those buggy nights, with sticky sour mix glueing my fingers together at 2 a.m. at a backyard seafood buffet on a plastic surgeon's estate, I knew something was coming. Even when socialites secretly gave me their phone numbers in front of their husbands while drinking Cape Cods out of a plastic *Starbucks* cup, I knew something was coming. Even when I was told to carry six cases of champagne up eight flights of stairs at a musician's birthday party when the elevator broke, I knew something was coming. That broken elevator night, the master of ceremonies didn't show up, and guess who had to take the microphone in his black uniform that he sweat through from vertically schlepping booze? Yes, even then I knew something was coming.

As a bartender, you never know what to expect from a private party, but this is where the acting comes in handy. You show up, you pour, you dump your tip jar in your bag, and you go home. You develop a thick skin. It's like auditioning... minus the humiliation.

Once I was hired for a family's backyard party in the suburbs. I didn't know what to expect, but nonetheless, I was in my zone. This family was not like any I had worked for ever. I mean ever. They were warm, friendly, generous, and all of the guests were amazing. Some turned into clients for future parties and some became friends. I had been invited to be the bartender a few summers in a row for the same gathering and guests. On the third summer, after knowing everyone quite comfortably, I spoke to Jaclyn Hunt for the first time about her work. We had known each other from these gatherings and other parties I had poured for, but we finally talked about her exciting, life-changing work as a life coach. She was not the spray-tanned, Clorox-toothed, "*Audi*" type of life coach that avoids carbs while drinking spirulina. She is a real-life coach — a cognitive life coach to be exact. If you need to Google that, go for it. I found her to be inspiring, supportive, optimistic, "seeing the greatness in everyone" type of life coach. She talked to me about "the feeling." "The feeling" you get when you make contact with a client. It isn't something you can use words to describe. "The feeling" was the thing that makes a wizard know he has powers. "The feeling" is a combination of a baby being born, winning the lottery, and getting picked to enter *Studio 54.*

After she got to know more about my experience, my work outside of booze, my approach, and my career intentions, we decided to talk about working together. Fast forward to several months later, and many lengthy conversations, certifications, and client shadowings, etc., I was less of a bartender now and more of a certified cognitive coach. Victory was upon me. I was on my way to find "the feeling."

One of my first clients that I met was hesitant to meet me, to say the least. She stayed in her room for most of the hour that we had planned to meet. Her parents kept me entertained with lemon tea and the full verbal Wikipedia presentation dedicated to their daughter. A tough no nonsense 30-year-old, who took no bullshit from anyone. I was told she had all types of professionals visit the house for years, but she sent them all running like a babysitter who saw a ghost. As with many of my current clients, she had not connected with many of the "helpers" who had visited over the years. After you've been doing this work long enough, you meet a few people who work with individuals on the spectrum who should not be working with them. I once attended a meeting with one of my clients for some employment support. This organization primarily assists people on the spectrum with employment, resume, interview preparation, etc. This employment counselor was extremely rude, and I believe at that exact moment, she was having the worst day of her life. Let's call her Linda. Linda spoke very fast and wanted to get to lunch. She made references to being hungry and was staying longer to "help" us. My client, who was diagnosed with Asperger's syndrome, quickly became anxious and confused. He had already been struggling with communication and had great difficulty accepting unwarranted feedback. I remained positive and collected for as long as I could. I guess it was that acting thing that kicked in again.

At one point, she squawked at my client holding a yellow highlighter, and asked," Are you paying attention?!"
He was visibly shut-down. After Linda's outburst, he was under-

standably done for the day. At this point, he should have held up a store sign that read "Sorry, we're closed." He was over her, but not as much as I was.

"Excuse me Linda," I said in my best Mid-Atlantic theatre voice. "Have you ever considered working at the DMV in New Jersey?"

Linda hates me.

Back to the kitchen. My new client finally decided to emerge from her bedroom. Her arms were folded and she sat across from me. She was sizing me up like she was thinking about which voodoo doll to use later that resembled me the most. I continued speaking with her parents. Her mom's body language anticipated embarrassment that her daughter would certainly provoke.

The grouchy client interrupted, "What the hell do you know about Autism? You're not autistic!...Well?!"

Her snarky teenage comment broke the silence. Her parents waited to see who had the next move. What this family didn't know was that I had auditioned for The William Morris Agency. Once you get through those doors, you fear nothing.

"No, I am not autistic, but I'll tell you why I do this... I wish I could say it's because of all the articles I have read about autistic adults, but there aren't any articles. I am here to advocate and motivate. You just have to give me a chance. You probably feel like people don't give you a chance. That's why I'm here."

Her arms unfolded. It only took a few minutes for her parents to excuse themselves and they went for a walk. Moments later, my new client and I were laughing and drinking tea together like two old British women. I learned so much about her in 30 minutes. She told me she liked coffee because tea was "just hot water." She shared with me her stories of wine tastings, reality shows, and her Juicy Couture tracksuits from high school. She was ready to work and we did.

I left that day not only with several text messages from her, thanking me, but I left with "the feeling." This was the same one Jaclyn had described. It was the one I was expecting even when I didn't know where bartending would take me.

You see, even with her missing body parts, her marble polishing body wash, and her updates, Victory has wings. Huge, extraordinary wings; wings so big, that airplanes get jealous. I trusted my journey. Even while making Long Island iced teas, I recognized my wings. Even after eight auditions in four days and never getting one of those jobs, my wings are still here. I recognized my potential and I continue to recognize it in others. This isn't a magical spell. It's using confidence, love, faith, trust, and okay, maybe some magic. I believe it is up to us to remind others of their wings. Remind them of their potential. Remind them of their worth. Remind them of their significance. Remind them of their importance. But most of all, remind them of "the feeling," because like our wings, it is there.

CHAPTER 5

Teach Real-Life Skills

What differentiates a coach from a therapist is that a coach focuses on real-life skills training and takes a more hands-on approach in a client's life. A therapist is a bit more limited in what they can do for a patient. Likewise, therapy is a more passive approach of emotional exploration and understanding. There is, of course, a similar aspect in coaching given the personal nature of the problems we are attempting to solve, but the greater goal and focus is to teach the client real-life skills and give them the tools they need to implement those skills out in the real world. The majority of my clients are seen through video conferencing software. That allows them to bring me into their homes, places of employment, and various social situations that a therapist or psychiatrist does not have access to. The technology today allows us to get out of the stuffy, clinical setting of a therapist's office, and instead, we can witness what is going on with a client in real time. The same is true for in-person sessions. I can meet with a client in a coffee shop, at their home, at work, school, or any other social place that is conducive to our work. This is rarely done in therapy. As mentioned previously, therapy is wonderful. It is necessary and effective when used to treat specific issues. Life coaching in conjunction with therapy is even better. Each professional working with a client becomes an integral part of the team. The therapist works on the emotional and mental health aspect, the psychiatrist works on the chemical balance part, the case manger takes care of the pragmatic situation of managing the team, and depending on the individual client's needs, the list goes on and on. Notably, the very first thing that comes to mind that very few of these professionals understand how to teach in a thorough and complete manner is something that seems quite basic but in reality is very complex: social skills.

The number one priority when working with someone on the ASD spectrum is teaching the basic all the way up to the highly advanced nuances of social communication that they never intuitively learned growing up. Remember, ASD is a social and communicative disorder. Consequently, a social disorder in a highly social world can cause great distress in an individual. For example, lack of friendships, bullying, difficulty getting through school or having enough social ability to get through a job interview or maintain employment for an individual, who is otherwise intelligent in other areas, are only some of the major issues that stem from poor social skills. Still, simply because social skills do not come as intuitively to an ASD adult, they are still perfectly learnable if taught in a way that the individual best learns and responds to effectively. As Dr. Temple Grandin says in almost all of her works on ASD, everyone learns differently. The majority of neurotypicals learn by observing others. The vast amount of people on the spectrum learn in other ways, such as in the written word, verbally, auditory, in a tactile way, or visually with images. There are other ways of learning as well but these are the most common. Very few with ASD, but not all, can learn the subtle social expressions until they are taught to recognize and communicate in that non-verbal language. All in all, social skills involve recognizing, interpreting, and responding to another person's verbal and non-verbal communication, and then successfully responding in a socially appropriate way. To have advanced social skills requires the ability to begin, continue, and terminate an interaction at will successfully, in a way that is considered socially appropriate by the individual or group of people one is interacting with at any given time.

Mistakenly, many clients believe that communication is talking at length about a topic of interest. They are then bored when it becomes someone else's turn to speak about something that interests them. Often, but not always, clients with ASD tend to monologue about their special interests rather than communicating in a more socially appropriate way. For instance, a client who enjoys anime, a Japanese style cartoon or animation, may talk about a favorite show they enjoy and dominate the conversation until the individual or group they are speaking to gets tired and disengages. They may even avoid the client in the future so that they do not have to listen to a long story about a topic they may not necessarily have an interest in themselves. Clients often become discouraged that they can't find friends or people to talk to about their very specific interests. The mistake comes from the notion that you need to share very specific things in common with people in order to communicate with them and enjoy their company. There may be times where you find someone who likes anime, or whatever your specific interest is, and you'll have a long discussion about it with that other person and enjoy yourself thoroughly. However, the vast majority of interactions in life are based more on immediate commonalities and, most importantly, reciprocity.

Well-developed communication skills involve being capable of having interactions with people in a reciprocal way. This means that one person begins talking while the other person actively listens. To actively listen means to hear the speaker's words, show the speaker you are listening and understanding, and participating by asking for more information, clarification, or indicating in some fashion to continue or cease. The speaker, as a rule of thumb, should not speak for more than about a paragraph of information, or 5-7 sentences, before checking in with the active listener. The speaker is observing the listener to make sure they are following what the speaker is saying, retaining interest in what the speaker is communicating, and checking to see if the listener has something to ask or add to the conversation or to encourage the speaker to continue. When two people are interacting properly, the listener has just as much power to guide the conversation as the speaker. Once the listener obtains the opportunity to speak, they will also speak for approximately a paragraph of information, and then check in with the active listener and repeat the process. This type of communication is the most rewarding and sustainable type of interaction you can have with another person. It can be much more rewarding than talking about a topic of interest at length with no feedback or exchange. The purpose of communication is to have a back and forth exchange of information, but the interaction in it of itself is also what is rewarding.

Here is an illustration of how this type of proper communication could occur between two individuals:

Speaker 1: "Hello! How are you today?"

Speaker 2: "I am well, how about you?"

Speaker 1: "My day is going swimmingly! I just got back from a haircut and am looking forward to grabbing a pizza. My plan is to go home to watch my favorite show, *The Curse of Oak Island*. It is about these treasure hunters seeking out the secrets of the Island's past and their hope to find some amazing long lost treasure. I am so entertained by watching this show. Have you seen it?"

Speaker 2: "I have seen it. It is not my cup of tea. Still, I am happy you enjoy it."

Speaker 1: "Why thank you! So, enough about my show. What do you like to watch?"

Speaker 2: "Well, since you asked, I am very much into *The Walking Dead*. It is about a zombie apocalypse and the crazy survival adventures that ensue. I watch it every week. I am looking forward to seeing what happens next. Are you a fan?"

Speaker 1: "No, but it does sound interesting. Perhaps I will check it out!"

Speaker 2: "Great! Let me know if you do. I would love to hear your thoughts. I need to get going now but it was great to talk to you. I hope we run into each other again soon."

Speaker 1: "Likewise! Have a great day."

Speaker 2: "You too!"

Let's analyze this conversation. We have the initial engagement with greetings from both speakers. Speaker 1 elaborates on his day and stays within the 5 to 7 sentence rule. He then checks in with the active listener. The active listener answers the question briefly and throws the ball back to Speaker 1's court, meaning, he gives Speaker 1 another turn to speak. They successfully have a back and forth about favorite television shows, even though they do not like the same exact programs. They demonstrate acknowledgment, gratitude, patience, and active listening skills. Finally, Speaker 2 decides to terminate the interaction. Speaker 1 recognizes that and accepts the termination with a farewell greeting. Speaker 2 concurs and the interaction is over. Keep in mind, this is a very simple example of a successful back and forth conversation.

Now, there is much more to communication than a verbal exchange of information. The aspect of communication that most adults with ASD struggle with is the non-verbal aspect of communication. Non-verbal communication consists of exchanging information in ways other than speaking aloud. This can include eye contact, body language, the tone or inflection in the voice, or even saying one thing and meaning the complete opposite. Interestingly, many of my client's parents have come to me and told me they want their adult child to learn how to make eye contact. For an individual who doesn't understand that eye contact is a tool to read and communicate non-verbal information, simply telling them to make eye contact throughout the years results in a stone cold killer stare, rather than what I call purposeful eye contact. We should not just teach ASD adults to stare at people. We have to teach the very specific nuances of nonverbal communication in order for them to understand why they are making eye contact and how to utilize that eye contact as a very valuable tool that will make them excel at communicating effectively. For instance, a client must first be taught to get used to making eye contact by looking at themselves in the mirror. That is the smallest and least stressful goal when beginning to teach proper eye contact. Then, we must ask the client to look for emotional cues in their own eyes and faces to see what they may be unintentionally showing the world so that we can shift to intentionally showing what we wish people to see. Next, the client needs practice looking for non-verbal information in another person's eyes and face. That's something we do in the life coaching session. We role play reading each other using purposeful eye contact. Once the client learns that eye contact has a purpose much deeper than the fact that they "just have to do it," they respond and can learn to excel at it. Soon the client uses eye contact to look for valuable non-verbal information in the person they are communicating with and uses the information to formulate their next move. They are also able to use eye contact as a way to convey interest, meaning, and intention in every day communication with people. Once purposeful eye contact is understood, we can move on to different types of non-verbal communication skills.

What does teaching purposeful eye contact look like? Let's take a look at the below example:

Coach: "Hi Fred. How are you today?"
Fred: "Okay."
Coach: "Are you sure? You are looking away from me. Does that mean you are bored with what I am saying?"
Fred: "No!"
Coach: "Okay. May I ask you a question?"
Fred: "Sure."
Coach: "How am I feeling right now?"
Fred: "I don't know."
Coach: "I can teach you a trick to find some clues. If you look at me, you might see some indicators in my face and posture that may hint at my internal state."

::Fred looks at the coach. He sees a big smile and hands open on the

table.::

Fred: "You look happy."
Coach: "Exactly right! All it took was a look for you to figure that out. Do you think we can work on looking at people you are speaking with to find out all the wonderful information you may have been missing out on in the past."
Fred: "Well, yeah!"

In this case, Fred needed to be encouraged to utilize the non-verbal tool of eye contact. When he saw the non-verbal signal of a smile, he was quickly able to determine the mood of his coach. That can be nearly impossible if he didn't choose to look. Now that Fred understands that by looking he can obtain valuable information, he may be more willing in the future to look at the people he is attempting to communicate with on a daily basis.

Another type of non-verbal communication skill is body language. Depending on our cultural backgrounds, we all "speak" to a varying degree with our bodies. It isn't magic that our mother's know when something is wrong long before we say anything to them. They can read our body language quite clearly. Many on the spectrum feel that neurotypicals communicate via telepathy and they are left in the dark. Well, it isn't telepathy. It is simply a form of non-verbal communication. Our bodies can show if we are opened or closed to a conversation. Likewise, our bodies can indicate if we are in a good mood or a foul mood. Posture, limb positioning, leaning forward or back, scrunching up or stretching out tells us so much about a person and what they want the world to see. Often, an adult with ASD doesn't notice these cues in others, and because of their tendency to confound things more, they often use mismatched body language to their own internal state, causing others to misinterpret or make assumptions about the ASD individual that may not necessarily be true. For instance, someone who avoids eye contact, crosses their arms, and lowers their brow is usually desiring to avoid conversation. Most adults with ASD are starving for conversation and company, but they are inadvertently sending off a non-verbal signal that keeps people away. They then make the assumption that no one wants to speak with them, when the reality is they send a signal that kept people away. This is just one example of many possibilities. What we need to do is teach and provide adults with ASD thorough and complete training on non-verbal communication skills to empower them to have more understanding and control of any potential social situation. Let's take a look at the coach instructing Anna to look at herself in the mirror in order to show her what he current body language is saying to the listener.

Coach: "Anna, how do you feel right now?"
Anna: "I am feeling happy."
Coach: "Did you know that it is difficult for me to read that you are happy?"
Anna: "But I just told you that I am happy."
Coach: "Yes, but you do not look happy. Take a look in this mirror. What would you say your body language is telling me here?"
Anna: "Oh, I am frowning and I am slumped over to the side."
Coach: "And what am I doing to indicate to you that I am happy?"
Anna: "You are smiling."
Coach: "Try to match your internal state to your outward appearance!"
::Anna smiles.::

Now again, this is a very simple example of a concept that can get very complex as we get into more elaborate emotions and combinations of emotions. Many on the spectrum do not realize you can feel and express multiple emotions all at once in a non-verbal way. You can be devastated that you just lost a loved one but still laugh at a joke on the television. Similarly, you can be angry with a loved one but still hug them when they get bad news unrelated to your argument. Emotions are complex, but our ability to teach how to match our internal state with our external nonverbal communication repertoire is quite doable for everyone on the spectrum.

Another real-life skill we want to see all of our clients achieve is independent living. This requires adequate executive functioning skills. Some examples of executive functioning are planning, organizing, time management, transitioning, memory, emotional control, attention, initiation, and following through on goals. A life coach can help build these skills in a client by breaking them down into smaller pieces and creating a template for each of these skills. The template can then be used as a valuable tool in a variety of situations so that the client can work through those situations as independently as possible to achieve success in the future. It is important to note that many parents inadvertently become the executive functioning aspect for their children. They may get their child out of bed in the morning or make appointments for them. Perhaps the parent is the child's walking calendar and memory. While this is sometimes quicker and more convenient in the moment, we have to do our best to get the child to build their own executive functioning skills in order to get as close to independence as possible.

Let's work through some possibilities in terms of building executive functioning skills in a client. Planning, for instance, requires pre-contemplation: "Gee, I'm starting to get hungry." The client is feeling hungry but is not yet ready to put any thought or effort into solving this developing issue. Now, if their mom or dad always provides lunch, then the executive functioning skill of planning lunch independently will not develop. Next is contemplation: "I need lunch." The client is now actively thinking about what he or she needs. This is where we actually get to the planning part: "I bought bread, lettuce and cold cuts at the grocery store yesterday. I will make a sandwich." This planning stage can be as detailed or concise as the individual client requires it to be. Some clients will need a descriptive step-by-step plan to make a sandwich, while others can put the pieces together a little more easily. The coach determines how detailed we need to get for each particular issue and develops the plan along with the client accordingly. Finally, the action of making the sandwich takes place and the need is fulfilled and the executive functioning skill has been successfully implemented. The coach's job is to help the client learn how to go through all of these stages of pre-contemplation to action, as well as help the client learn how to make step-by-step plans that will eventually be generalized to a variety of planning situations in that client's life.

In terms of organization, there are many strategies we can use. We have to tailor it to what the individual responds to and we sometimes have to get very creative. Something I like to work on with clients is a shared calendar. In the beginning, I work on the calendar with the client, and eventually, they take over more and more responsibility. The calendar can be handwritten or online, include colors, pictures, reminders, notifications, something more tactile like an old school planner with stickers, or as most clients prefer, their cell phone calendar. The calendar is a great tool for time management planning. Notably, the autistic mind has trouble with the concept of time. A calendar helps visualize time in a way that many with ASD cannot envision in their mind. I could most likely tell you approximately what time it is based on a variety of subconscious sensations at any given point in the day. When I wake up in the morning, I have an idea of what time it may be by the amount of light in the room, if I heard the garbage trucks drive by, if I heard church bells in the distance, if the heat kicked on, if my husband is still in bed or if he emerged. Very often, someone on the spectrum does not always subconsciously or consciously attune to all of these factors as clearly as a neurotypical might. Therefore, we have to provide more concrete ways of visualizing time. In addition to visualizing time, we have to come up with ways to estimate how much time it will take to complete certain tasks. I know that it takes me 10 minutes to empty the dishwasher. I never had to sit down and think about this. I just know I can fit that chore in when I have a 15 minute break between sessions or if I have to head out in 20 minutes. An ASD adult may not necessarily "know" this as intuitively, so we have to specifically figure out how long a variety of chores will take, and then we can build up that time management journal until the client is able to generalize and estimate time more effectively when they have a variety of chores to compare a new chore or activity with. The same goes for work projects, home projects, how long a dinner out might take, and much more.

The same mechanism that prevents someone on the spectrum from sensing subconscious cues as to what time it might be plays a part in having difficulty transitioning from one task or event to another. The neurotypical generally is preparing themselves for the transition long before the transition takes place. The ASD adult often reacts strongly because the transition seems to come out of nowhere. The key here is to help the client recognize the transition process earlier so that there are no surprises. For instance, a local park near my house has train tracks. I always notice these train tracks when I enter the park. Once in a while, a train goes by and it's loud, but I knew that was a possibility because I had already noticed the train tracks. An adult with ASD can miss the train tracks completely, and when that train comes barreling down, horns blaring, they can be quite startled by the unpredictable transition from a quiet, peaceful day in the park to a loud, overstimulating, and stressful experience. I bounce back immediately because I've expected the transition, but my client struggles for a while. Over time, I point out possible triggers and alternatives to what may happen at the park that day. Soon the client learns to scan and look for possible alternatives as well. Over time, the train no longer startles them because they have learned to prepare for various transitional possibilities. Remember, this is just one very specific example of a concept that requires practice in many various circumstances.

Now, let's move on to memory. This executive function confuses many parents because the adult child often memorizes vast amounts of information. The ASD mind likes logical problems with clear-cut solutions, and memorization is the part of the brain that often overcompensates for social struggles and executive functioning difficulties which are much more complex processes. Neurotypical memory is tied to emotion and is chunked into larger pieces that are easier to remember than individual pieces of information. So, for example, I can remember my brother coming home from the hospital when I was 3 years old, even though I can barely remember anything else from that young age. It was a powerful emotional moment that my memory is tied to, so I remember it vividly. Different things stimulate emotional responses in those with ASD, so they may remember different situations vividly, such as their grandmother's earrings as she was holding him or a stimulating show that produced great joy. Memory is complex and I can't give you exact examples of what goes through each individual's brain. We just have to keep in mind that memory is stronger when there is an emotion attached to it.

Neurotypicals think in wholes while ASD adults think in parts. The ASD adult is memorizing vast amounts of information and it therefore might seem like they are processing slower than the average person. The reality is they are processing a huge amount of information at an incredible rate to keep up with us neurotypicals who combine parts into wholes and remember the whole. A good example is a client who told me the ocean is stressful. To me, the ocean is one of the most relaxing things on Earth — an almost endless void. That client told me he sees every individual wave, hears every individual sound and noise nearby and in the distance. He is so overloaded with information that it makes it nearly impossible to remember small social details. However, it is possible to teach connecting parts to wholes. It needs to be specifically taught and practiced. Now, that same client loves gazing out into the vastness of the ocean.

Being a social and communicative disorder, ASD brings with it many frustrations that can make emotional control very difficult at times. We've previously discussed how much information people on the spectrum are processing at any given moment. The information and sensory processing alone can be exhausting. Add to that the societal demands and expectations along with the individual's own internal state of being, needs, wants, desires and expectations of him or herself — it is no wonder emotional control can sometimes be difficult for someone on the spectrum. When your client is constantly on the verge of being overwhelmed, it may seem that the client "snaps" without warning. The truth is, there was a lot that went into that emotional break. It is my belief that we should work towards easing these stressors in life, and then we will find a major improvement in a client's ability to regulate his or her emotions.

There are an infinite amount of possible examples to illustrate emotional breaks and how to ease the many stressors that lead up to those breaks. It is a struggle to find one example that would demonstrate this concept completely. However, the first thing that comes to mind is bullying. The majority of my clients have been bullied at some point in their lives. The trauma associated with that type of treatment runs deep. Let's say part of the bullying was repeatedly being called "stupid" whenever a social mistake was made at school. Any time that client was called "stupid," the shame, embarrassment and anxiety would build. There would be significant emotional damage. Fast forward years later at the client's place of employment. An angry customer calls the client "stupid" for making a minor error while ringing up her groceries. The client immediately has an angry emotional outburst directed at anyone who gets in the way. Subsequently, the client gets fired from his job. Instead of working towards healing the emotional pain, the firing further supports the "stupid" label in the client's mind, and the client continues to live at the edge of maintaining some semblance of emotional control. So much could have been done to help ease the client's pain and heal the initial trauma. First, the bullying could have been identified and dealt with at the time of exposure. It was not. Over the years, it was placed in the past without any opportunity to heal those wounds. The job opportunity was a big boost to the client's self-confidence, and all was well until he was called "stupid." If he was in a more understanding environment, he could have been given a second chance. Similarly, his trigger could have been identified and he could have been reassured that he wasn't stupid and given evidence of many of his work accomplishments. It could take a significant amount of time, but emotional control can improve with the proper supports put into place, including a continual monitoring of the client's personal triggers, eventually progressing towards healthier responses.

Another important executive functioning skill is attention. Many on the spectrum have also been diagnosed with ADHD. Attention issues can have an effect on many aspects of life, most notably, communication and staying on task. Those with attention difficulties have trouble following and engaging in conversations as well as beginning and seeing a task through to completion. The trick here is to make these areas of life more rewarding. It is much easier to focus on someone or something when we are interested and find it rewarding. For instance, many clients can play and focus on video games for hours on end. They are both engaging and rewarding, not to mention fun. The more we can make real-life rewarding and successful through coaching, attention tends to improve. Therapy can also help with ADHD symptoms along with some medications; however, I always try to find ways to make life more engaging first and to utilize the other services when a client needs something more.

One of the most difficult things to do in life is to get started. This was true for me in writing this very book. Taking initiative is an executive functioning skill that many with ASD struggle with. The spontaneity necessary to come up with an idea of what to do without prompting is complex and often not readily on an ASD individual's mind or is completely absent. Teaching someone to take initiative requires a repertoire of initiative taking possibilities in various realms of life, including home, school, work, and in social situations. For example, I often work with couples where one is on the spectrum and the other is neurotypical. Quite often, the NT would like the ASD partner to take initiative with household chores. Together with the client, we come up with possible chores that they can do on their own, without prompting from the significant other, that the ASD adult can realistically achieve successfully. For instance, making the bed. This particular client left for work after his wife and was the last to get out of bed in the morning. This was the perfect chore for the client to take initiative on and the spouse was pleasantly surprised when she arrived home to a made bed. Over time, we add more and more opportunities to take initiative and ways to identify these needs to the client, i.e. through reminders or notes, that these are initiative taking opportunities. Initiative taking may be more intuitive to an NT, but ASD adults can learn to recognize these instances and take initiative through repetition and practice until it becomes second nature.

The final executive functioning skill mentioned above is following through on goals. Life coaching is all about brainstorming, developing, setting, and achieving goals. It is so much more than simply following through. It is a complex, step-by-step approach that many clients do not have a built in template for and often get stuck along the way. For instance, many clients have a goal in mind but do not know where to start. Others may know where to start but get sidetracked on the journey. Still, others do not even have a clear vision of the goal they set for themselves. The first step in achieving goals is to brainstorm what that goal should be. It then needs to be well-defined and realistic to achieve for that individual. A detailed step-by-step plan to reach that ultimate goal should then be outlined so that the client can measure his or her progress along the way. Lastly, the goal is achieved and the process begins anew. Sometimes goals may not be realistic to the individual. For example, I often have clients come to me with the goal of becoming a video game designer because of their love of video games. Some clients can realistically achieve this goal. Others simply cannot. So instead of quashing a dream, I help the client to reframe and create a more realistic goal they can become passionate about and achieve. In this example, I would outline for the client all the steps necessary to become a video game designer. Together we would recognize the step that would be unrealistic and find a new path to a similar yet more doable goal conducive to the client's unique set of talents and abilities.

I often tell my clients a very relevant story from my own life. In high school, I had dreams of becoming a computer programmer because I enjoyed computers tremendously and I also liked a C++ class I was taking at the time. Once in college, I quickly realized that I could not do the high-level math required to get a degree in computer science. My path needed to divert towards my other strengths, and soon, I decided to switch my major to psychology. Once I graduated, I decided I needed more schooling to attain my new goal of becoming a marriage and family therapist. In my graduate studies, I became frustrated with the lack of training for autism spectrum disorders. I was inspired by a speaker at my school to forgo licensure as a therapist and instead become a life coach specifically for adults on the spectrum. And the rest is history. As you can see, my career goals transformed as I went. As long as we are on a path and strive towards some goal, we will always progress and grow. We just need to be open to the alternative paths life gives us along the way.

CHAPTER 6

Building Friendships from the Ground Up

Friendship is essential. Unfortunately, the world today has become a very lonely place for many. With the rise of the social media age, designed to connect the world in a way that it has never seen before, we have all become more isolated from deeper human social connections. The strongest connections often come from two or more people experiencing something together and coming out on the other side of it with a story to tell and shared memories. The first of these experiences is often our school years. We share classes, sports teams, the band or orchestra, the drama department, and various other after school activities. These events are where many close social connections are formed. As these activities disappear and more of our children are staying home alone, we lose much more than the activity itself — we lose opportunities for deeper social connections and human presence. This applies to everyone. Then, when you take a person with a social and communicative disorder and they have no idea how to navigate these increasingly rare situations, it can be disastrous to their social and emotional well-being. It breaks my heart each time I meet someone new who has zero friends. The majority of my clients come to me with few to no close friendships. It becomes my duty to first become friends with that client. They need and deserve a friend. We all require someone we can pick up the phone and call or someone to text when loneliness hits. This obligation that I've taken on is not a burden at all. It fills my life up with kind, interesting, fun, and overall amazing people from all over the world. The appreciation that mutually exists between us is so valuable and rewarding. For those who make friends easily, taking friendships for granted seems like such a waste to someone who is desperate for just one friend. I make certain that I appreciate every single client, and let me tell you, they make it so easy. When I teach clients to become my friend, we can then generalize what we learn together to form other rewarding peer relationships.

For most people, forming friendships is a very intuitive process. We usually don't think about it, it just happens. Simply because we don't think about it doesn't mean there isn't a process involved. Neurotypicals tend to automate things without even realizing it. Think back to our parts to wholes discussion in an earlier chapter. In order to teach someone on the spectrum how to make friends, we need to have a clear-cut, logical outline of all the different types of friendships and where they go on the friendship pyramid. As I just stated, friendships belong in a pyramid. The bottom of the pyramid is Level 1: acquaintances. The very top of the pyramid is Level 10: ourselves. We are our own ultimate relationship. The bottom of the pyramid includes a higher number friends and the very top of the pyramid is just one person. I will go through each level of friendship in the friendship pyramid below. These levels have been formulated through extensive talks and my work with many of clients over the years. It is important to place people at the proper level in our lives. If we do not, it can cause unintentional consequences. For example, many clients come to me desperate for a friend. Often, they are so eager to have a friend that when someone comes along, they quickly elevate them to a best friend and tend to smother the relationship before it has time to form properly. Every friendship must start at Level 1 and work up through each level step-by-step. When you meet someone new and immediately elevate them, there are almost always negative consequences, ranging from losing that potential friendship to being taken advantage of in a variety of possible ways. Let's go through each level of friendship one by one, how to stay at a level, how to advance a level, how to backtrack to a previous level, and how to maintain friendship boundaries over time.

Beginning with Level 1, acquaintances are essentially everyone we come in contact with throughout the day. An acquaintance can be the mail carrier, the checkout clerk, someone you see daily on the bus — basically, just about anyone. When I initially teach this concept, I'm immediately asked, "But what about strangers?" My response is that acquaintances are new people at the lowest level of trust. If we keep them there at that very low level, a stranger who you've just met is a low level acquaintance that we set very specific boundaries with in order to maintain safety from potential stranger dangers. Acquaintances are people in our lives that we generally only engage in small talk with and then move on with our day. For instance, you may say, "Hi!" to the mail carrier and then go into your house. You may nod to the woman on the bus whom you see each morning. Perhaps someone at the checkout counter cracks a joke and everyone laughs. While waiting in line for a movie, someone may comment on the weather and you may concur. These are extremely low level friendships that do not go beyond basic small talk and daily interactions. To stay at this level is to keep small talk basic, only see these people in the everyday situations that you typically encounter them, and disengage if they attempt to rise up a level by discussing very specific experiences rather than sticking to small talk topics. You have the power to keep someone at a level and the power to see if that person would like to rise up a level with you. Likewise, the other person has that same power to stay where the relationship is or test the waters in an attempt to rise up a level in your life.

Before continuing up the friendship pyramid, we must have a discussion on small talk. Many on the spectrum despise small talk because it seems fake and without purpose. My clients love to delve right into meaningful conversation. This may be appropriate in a professional setting like coaching or therapy so that we can get right to the issues at hand in a timely manner, but it is not appropriate in the real world with a low level friendship. Clients often do not see the point in talking about the weather or have repetitive boring discussions about gas mileage. The problem with hating small talk is that it is the key to lower level friendships. The misconception about small talk is that it appears, on the surface, to be meaningless. The reality is that small talk has a much richer purpose than we realize. This is why it is essential to discuss the importance of small talk as well as the greater meaning and purpose it holds in creating initial relationships.

First, small talk has purpose. On the surface it may seem that talking about the weather is a waste of time because we can just look out the window and see it, discussion over. Yes, of course the content of small talk is often boring or obvious. but its purpose and the meaning behind the content of the conversation is quite deep and complex. For instance, when someone new meets us, they have a decision to make. Do they engage with us or stay quiet? If they choose to engage, then they need an "in" to communicate. That "in" is usually small talk. Small talk is an indicator that a person finds you worthy enough to begin a conversation with and attempt to get to know you better. It means they would like to make you a Level one friendship in his or her life. It is the first move to elevate you from no relationship to a relationship.

Here is an example of a small talk interaction:

::Standing at a bus stop.::
Tom: "Boy, there sure was a lot of snow last night."
Suzy: "Yes, that's probably why the bus is late."
Tom: "I didn't even think of that. I hope it gets here soon. I am cold. Are you okay?"
Suzy: "Yes, I am fine. Thank you for asking."
Tom: "You are welcome." ::smiles::

As you can see, Tom made a statement about a common environmental observation. Suzy concurred and engaged in the small talk by adding another observation that was mutually relevant. This information was accepted by Tom who chose to take the interaction a bit further. He expressed his discomfort and asked about Suzy's well-being. Suzy graciously accepted his concern and closed out the conversation by making a statement indicating that she didn't want to continue. Tom replied politely and successfully accepted the cue to terminate the interaction with a non-verbal smile.

Remember, there are 4 options when in a friendship level with someone. You can stay at that level, advance up a level, backtrack to a lower level, and once a comfortable level is achieved, maintain the boundaries of that level. So, when a new person engages in small talk, it isn't about the topic they choose, it is about the fact that they are choosing to attempt a level raise with you and you have the opportunity to take it or leave it. So if it isn't about the topic they choose to engage in small talk, we can then find small talk much easier to utilize. For example, someone is talking about the weather. They are seeking out a relevant topic to the level you're currently at and showing that they wish to engage. If the target responds, the interaction is successful. The two then have the option to continue or stay at that level. Staying at the small talk, immediate surroundings and obvious commonalities level is Level 1. Pursuing the discovery of common interests is Level 2: the developmental stage.

Rising up a level in the friendship pyramid involves an attempt to develop something more than just a Level 1 acquaintance small talk friendship. Level 2 is actually a developmental stage where you purposely begin to discover common interests. For example, many men tend to ask about sports as one of their go-to level raising questions. Some people ask about work or family or anything they can think of that they might possibly have in common with this new person that they want to see if they can get closer with over time. We are now going beyond small talk into common interests. The level of trust in this stage does not go beyond revealing some interests and specifically talking about them. If you are having trouble finding commonalities or don't particularly like the other person's interests, you can backtrack a level and go back to small talk. If you are enjoying the other person's interests, you can stay at this level for a while and begin to learn more about each other's hobbies and interests. You may wish to continue to advance to a new level or you may feel comfortable here and stick to sports talk or any type of interest talk. The other person also has that choice. It is when two people both want to advance a level that it actually takes place. It also takes two people to maintain a level while it only takes one person to decide if they want to backtrack a level.

Let's go back to Tom and Suzy. Perhaps instead of closing out the conversation with Tom, Suzy decides to continue the conversation to get to know him better. Tom asked if she was okay:

Suzy: "Yes, I am fine. Thank you for asking. Hey! Are you also heading to the big festival downtown?"
Tom: "I sure am! I am really looking forward to listening to some good music, having some kettle corn, and, of course, the hot chocolate."
Suzy: "Wow! I love the music at these festivals. What's your favorite genre?"
Tom: "I'm into classic rock."
Suzy: "I am as well!"
Tom: "That's great!"

In this interaction, Suzy is looking to find commonalities with Tom. She is attempting to learn if rising up a friendship level is something she wants to pursue, and Tom is receptive to finding these commonalities as well. They can proceed this way to find out more or just discuss the new topic at hand.

We have now gone from small talk to common interests. These are still very low level relationships and the level of trust here does not go any further than revealing some of the things you are interested in. Now, if you would like to attempt to rise to Level 3, you must begin to find ways to share in and experience common interests with the Level 2 person. This is the point in time that you begin to go out of your way to spend time with each other. However, the amount of time you spend and the level of trust allowed here does not go beyond what the activity and interest require. Now, there is no set time frame in terms of how long going from Levels 1-3 takes. It could happen rapidly or take many months. As long as friendship isn't rushed or puts pressure on someone, it is developing at a typical pace. Quite often, Levels 1-3 are one-on-one friendships. Once small experiences are shared, it is very common for groups to form. Level 4 is the low level group stage based upon common interests. For example, a bunch of guys get together to play basketball or perhaps the girls do a dance class on Fridays. Maybe it is movie night for the gang. This is also the stage where other possibilities open up. You begin experimenting with more information. For instance, Level 4 friends may start to open up about slightly more personal information such as favorite foods, other interests, and have a desire to learn more of these things about other members of the friendship group. This is a pivotal stage that leads into more potentially intimate friendships in the future. It is important to note at this point that a healthy relationship pyramid keeps friendships at all levels. Not all will advance and some will move up and down levels multiple times perhaps throughout a lifetime. So there is no need for distress if, with certain people, you can only achieve a Level 4 or even lower friendship. There will always be someone to elevate higher as time goes on.

Now, let's say Suzy decides she is interested in spending some more time with Tom. She wants to get into that Level 3 zone so she tests the waters to see if Tom accepts:

Suzy: "Wow! I love the music at these festivals. What's your favorite genre?"
Tom: "I'm into classic rock."
Suzy: "I am as well!"
Tom: "That's great!"
Suzy: "I also like hot chocolate. Perhaps I can join you?"

Now Tom has the opportunity to accept or reject Suzy's question.

Tom: "Actually, I am meeting a friend at the festival. Perhaps we can get together another day?"
Suzy: "That would be great! Have fun at the festival."
Tom: "You too!"

Notice how even though Tom rejected Suzy's request, she still remained polite and enthusiastic. She did not get sad or argue with him. She respected his plans! Now what happens if Tom accepts her proposal?

Tom: "Actually, that would be wonderful. I'd love to have a hot chocolate with you and introduce you to my group of friends.
Suzy: "Awesome! I can't wait to meet them."

We achieved Level 3 and 4 here — sharing a common interest together and entering a larger group with similar interests. Remember, rejections are to be accepted and acknowledged just a gracefully as acceptances.

We now come to the next phase of friendship levels. Levels 5 through 8 are more intimate than the previous levels. Level 5 is the smaller, selective group stage. For example, you may be invited to a party by your Level 4 group of friends. You meet and interact with many people at Levels 1-4. As it gets later, the lower levels tend to leave the party and head home. Some of the Level 4's that stick around tend to get closer because they enjoy each other's company. Level 5 is achieved! A small, selective group within a group forms. The level of trust here is fluid. You may begin talking about hopes, dreams, and desires beyond the common interests conversations of the past. Then, the smallest group stage is Level 6. It usually comprises of 2-3 people and the relationship is closer and more intimate than previous relationships. Hopes, dreams, and desires are well known throughout the group. You begin sharing your past and your friends feel it vicariously through you. There may even be arguments and frustrations at this stage. Clashes occur from time to time because of the ripening of emotional closeness beginning to take place. Then, this leads into one on one time with selective members of this small group, Level 7. Platonic dinners or coffee as well as one on one activities become common. Perhaps a discussion about a serious problem in your life occurs because you respect and value your friend's advice. The level of trust here is still cautious but more open each time your friend proves him or herself trustworthy. Now, after all of that, perhaps months or years have gone by so that closeness and high levels of trust have been proven time and time again.

In our sample scenario, one of infinite possibilities, Tom and Suzy have spent a lot of time together. Suzy was welcomed into Tom's friendship group, and over the next few months, they have been spending more and more time alone together. They have both proved to each other that they can be trusted with feelings, hopes, dreams, and desires. It is here that Suzy asks Tom a very important question. She is afraid but also knows that he will be gentle with her feelings after all these months of building trust and having open communication.

Suzy: "Tom, we have been seeing each other for quite a few months now and I really want to ask you something."
Tom: "What is it?"
Suzy: "I was wondering if we could date exclusively?"
Tom: "I wanted to ask you the same question for months but was too scared you weren't ready to take that step. Of course I want to date you exclusively."
Suzy: "Oh I am so happy! Let's go celebrate!"
::They embrace::

We then enter Level 8, the best friend stage. This is the level where your heart opens up to the other person and his or her heart opens up to you. This is usually one or two people but could easily be more depending on the circumstances. These are the people who lift you up and make you even better than you already are on your own. They can be a shoulder to cry on, a trusted friend, advisor, mentor and/or buddy. The best friend is always there for you and is never further than a call away. The trust is high but never complete. Full trust is reserved only for yourself. We now reach one of the more complicated levels. Level 9 is close family and romantic relationships. This can be parents, siblings, spouses, even children. This includes those who took on those roles in your life. The reason this stage is complicated is because not everyone has close family. So there may be overlap from Level 8. The level of trust here is risky too because Level 9 friends usually know us our entire lives, so they are the only level that has the greatest amount of power to hurt or betray us both on purpose or inadvertently. We do not necessarily get to choose the people in this level, so it can be both one of the most rewarding levels as well as the most traumatic. The complexities of this level are often worked on in depth in the coaching session. For the autistic mind, the "if's" and "depends" are often the most complex of concepts to master. Level 9 is quite often a complex concept.

Finally, the ultimate level of friendship, the one person in your life to trust completely and fully, is yourself. No one knows you better than you. Self-actualization, self-trust, self-worth, and self-esteem are not selfish things to pursue but essential for a healthy relationship pyramid. You are at the apex of a solidly built foundation of friendships at all levels and you stand at the top ready to tackle the world. Always trust your gut, your head, and your heart. This level must be maintained and held to the highest of standards so that all relationships that fall below know what to strive for in your life. These levels are an excellent guideline for all of us to place the relationships in our lives in their rightful place. The purpose of creating a friendship pyramid is to have a concrete format for a concept that comes more intuitively to the average person. We cannot simply tell a person with ASD to go out and make friends. We need to outline what a friend is and where they belong in our lives. A friend is not a one size fits all type of concept. Each friend is unique and belongs in a very specific level of our lives. As long as we keep friends at the appropriate level based on the criteria listed above, we have the very best chances of keeping ourselves safe from betrayal and fulfilled on a variety of emotional levels.

CHAPTER 7

The Development of Romantic Relationships

"How do I get a girlfriend?" This is the number one question I am asked by most new male clients. One of the top reasons adults on the spectrum reach out to me is because they are desperate for a romantic relationship. This can be true for both male and female clients; however, it is much more difficult for a male with ASD to find a romantic partner than it is for a female. This is true for neurotypicals as well. Yet, there are differences between males and females on the spectrum since the brain structure is quite varied and society treats males and females very differently. We will discuss the major differences between men and women with ASD in another section of this book. For the purposes of this chapter, we will focus more on the male perspective in seeking out a romantic relationship. Still, what we learn here can be applied to females as well, or anyone regardless of gender or sexuality. It is important to keep in mind that not everyone desires a romantic relationship and that is perfectly valid. We only pursue it if that is what the client wants. So, before we enter a romantic relationship, I always advise clients to keep in mind and utilize the levels of friendship we learned in the previous chapter. You go through each of those levels with a romantic interest just as you would with a platonic friendship, with the addition of potentially more physical connection as well as the possibility of cohabitation and/or marriage in the future. Cohabitation is different from having a roommate, which is a platonic relationship. Both cohabitation and marriage bring with them a bond and closeness between two people that goes beyond even the best friend level of friendship.

Remember, as we rise in friendship levels, we go from small talk to discussing interests to engaging each other with ideas. These types of discussions play a part in creating an air of romance in a relationship. Romance is a type of excitement or mystery about the other person and the future of the relationship. It's exciting to meet someone new and discover if the two of you will one day be committed to each other in a high level way. First, however, we must start at the beginning. Romance, in the low level small talk phase, is full of compliments and gestures of affection such as small gifts and flowers. Flirting is the ultimate small talk activity of romance. It involves teasing, touching, joking around with each other, and small hints of romantic interest and future possibilities become the fuel that runs these early romantic relationships. If both people enjoy these flirtatious activities, one or the other may indicate a desire to move up a level. Once you rise up a few levels into the experience stage. you are continuing the small talk behaviors but also including romantic experiences such as a date to the movies, an activity such as bowling together, or perhaps having a nice meal with each other. The romantic experience level can last quite a long time. Likewise, dating is an activity we do with another person designed to see if they are long-term relationship material. We place ourselves in a variety of experiences with the other person in order to see if we are compatible on various levels and interested in pursing the relationship on a long-term basis. This could lead to cohabitation, marriage, or even living separately but committed to each other for the long-term. It may also mean you discover that you are not good for each other and you go your separate ways. There is no right or wrong arrangement. It must only be a mutually agreed upon situation.

Not long ago I had a client who did a lot of work on himself. He had low self-confidence, depression, and yet he had a very high desire for a romantic relationship. He felt, in the beginning, that a romantic relationship would solve everything. The fact of the matter was that he needed to do a lot of work on himself before he was ready for that kind of journey. So eventually, I was able to convince him to work hard, lose weight, become more confident and able to believe compliments that came his way. Time and time again, he stepped out of his comfort zone so that he could build himself up in a way that he never had before. Eventually, he was ready to get into the dating scene. It was a rocky start. Every rejection felt tortuous and he took those rejections very personally. He often became very attached to a girl before the relationship even had time to form. At times, he was willing to date and accept women that were just not healthy relationship material because he felt he couldn't do any better. Many of us have been there. Through all of this, he learned and grew and didn't let rejection or failed relationships stop him. That was when he finally met not only the girl of his dreams, but she felt she found her dream guy! This didn't happen overnight. They talked for a while on a dating app until she was comfortable enough to meet in person. Their first date was very rocky with both of them left a little confused. They both kept trying, and in the process, they got to know each other, enjoyed each other's company and got very close. They didn't go exactly in order with the levels of friendship but they pretty much hit every one at some point. The moral of this particular story is that first we need to work on ourselves, our own ultimate relationship, before we can truly build a healthy and rewarding romantic relationship. We also have to realize that we do not attach ourselves to the first person we date or the first person that gives us attention. We need to be picky and take our time. Relationships can't be built in a day — at least not intimate, healthy relationships. If you want something long-term and sustainable, you need to take your time and be picky about who you choose as a potential romantic interest. You also have to remember that the choice must be mutual.

After months, perhaps years, of dating, two people who are committed to each other often become best friends or achieve Level 8 friendship. That means the relationship has progressed beyond atmosphere and experience and has advanced to ideas.

When we share hopes, dreams, and plans for the future together, we are interacting at a very high level with each other. As our lives become intertwined, we begin to take on more and more responsibility for each other. These responsibilities are often things that were only done by our parents for us as we were growing up. We now graduate to a more adult form of caring for another person and being cared for in return. This is the moment when a significant other becomes a Level 9 relationship. It is when you take a best friend and go just a little further by purposely choosing to be responsible for each other in most realms of life. When you reach Level 9, you trust and commit to each other, and you know that you are now an individual as well as part of a unit. This is an extremely high level of friendship and intimacy. Achieving this level of intimacy often leads to marriage. I recommend taking approximately 2 years to reach this level of intimacy with a romantic interest. It could take more time, but I have found 2 years is a reasonable amount of time to rise up the levels to this height of intimacy. Then, if marriage is desired, I also recommend a year's engagement to solidify the intimacy and create a next life phase plan for your life together as a couple.

Take another client relationship further along in the process. This couple met after my client relocated from California to New York City. We both agreed he needed a new environment to find the right relationship. New York City proved the place to be. To his surprise, he found someone within a few months of his move. They hit it off and are now living together in an apartment. The next step is, of course, for them to get engaged. They are both already making plans for their future together, and they possibly want pets, children, and eventually a retirement. They are very close to the engagement period of their relationship. Now, he isn't following my exact timeline because every relationship is different. Still, they are continually progressing forward as a couple. When you continually move forward, that's a sign of a very healthy relationship. If you are stuck, it is time to communicate and figure out how to keep the relationship moving in the right direction. Never stand idly by while a relationship is going nowhere or the other person in that relationship could be making their own plans. You must continually discuss, actively work on, and promote growth and change in your evolving relationship.

Now that we know the theory behind achieving this high level romantic relationship, we should now discuss how to go about finding a romantic interest. These days, people tend to meet at school, work, or some other regular activity location such as the gym. Environments such as these are conducive to having ample time to work up through the levels of friendship. Still, people do successfully meet in other environments such as a bar or nightclub. I do not promote this, but it does happen and can be successful. Today, many people date online. We cannot escape the social media age. This is where people go to specifically seek out a significant other, so we must consider it an option when finding a relationship is one of our goals. Meeting someone in person is easiest because we can simply work through the levels of friendship over time. Meeting someone online or using a dating app to find a potential significant other requires creating a dating profile and essentially advertising yourself to potential romantic interests. Many of my clients go about this task, and then when a match occurs, they want to fully commit to this new person as if this is the only opportunity that will arise. It makes sense when we are desperate for a relationship because we tend to take anything we can get. For example, if I were starving, I may choose food that I would never eat if I were satiated. When we are starving for a relationship, we can easily make a poor choice. This is why we must date in order to discover, through slowly moving up levels, if this person is truly compatible with us.

Usually, before this happens, we go through quite a few people before we find "the one.". It is not unheard of but extremely uncommon to fall in love with and remain with the first person you start dating. For someone who may be desperate for a relationship, this can be extremely disheartening. The fact is, we all must go through the process of hookups, dating, and very often rejection. Today, hookups are part of the culture. Many women and men are not yet ready to begin a long-term, committed relationship, but they still desire the company and closeness that comes with a hookup. In the online dating world, the majority of matches are going to be people seeking out a hookup, not necessarily want those who want to date. It is important to understand this when you match up with people online. This allows you the opportunity to also agree to the hookup or to continue looking until you find someone that wants to get to know you and date you with the possibility of building up to a Level 9 relationship. It is important to remember that even if you fall in love with someone, they may not necessarily feel the same way. It happens quite often in relationships where one person wants more and the other person does not. The sad consequence of looking for a relationship and dating is that we run a very high risk of rejection. Rejection is part of life. When you're on the spectrum and have suffered more than the average amount of rejections in life, it can be devastating to be rejected, especially if you really care about the other person. Still, the alternative is to give up completely and not date at all if you want to avoid rejection. Rejection even hurts if you don't particularly like the other person. It's the rejection that hurts, that makes us feel like there is something inherently wrong with us. The truth is that there is nothing wrong with us at all, it just takes time and a great deal of effort to seek out the person that is compatible with our unique way of being. So if you're ready to embark on a dating adventure to meet new people and hopefully come across the one you will spend your life with, you must be prepared for some rejection, both receiving and giving, along the way.

When I was in college, my brother was sick with a type of cancer. He is perfectly fine and healthy today. Anyway, during that time I was really focused on my studies as a way to cope, and I would go sit with my brother during his treatments between classes. Needless to say, it was one of the roughest times of my life. Now, during this time, I was in a class and I was getting very irritated that this guy kept looking back at me. I felt tired, sad, and very angry over my brother's illness and the suffering he had to go through. So when this guy in class kept looking at me, my blood began to boil. Eventually class ended and this brave guy comes up to me and hands me a note with all of his information. Back then, we didn't do Facebook, but he had written down his email and AOL screen name. I was just so caught off guard. I was deeply entrenched in my family struggles and I just blankly stared at him, handed the paper back. and said, "Sorry, I am already in a relationship." I walked away, and as I turned back, I saw the saddest face of rejection I have ever seen in my life. It still haunts me that I didn't reject him in a better way. It was true, I was in a relationship with my now husband. Still, I could have been happier, flattered, and gentle with this brave man's courage to approach me. I did a horrible job of rejecting and I'd like to think if I could do it over again, I would do a much better job. I have had to do rejecting after the fact, and while it may not always be perfect, I strive to keep the other person's feelings in mind because we all face rejection at some point or another.

So, this poor guy did not pick up on any of my non-verbal signals. I was angry, sad, depressed, and who knows what else. I was on my way to go sit with my brother during his treatment, and then all of a sudden this guy is in front of me, handing me a note. From my perspective, I just wanted to get out of there — not necessarily away from this guy, just away. When I rejected him, I was already in a relationship, and it was just the completely wrong time to approach me. Much can be learned from this story. Keep in mind, you should always reject with kindness and compassion, but at the same time be firm. Do not leave anything open for interpretation. Also, remember that everyone has something going on in their lives. I rejected this guy because I was not in the mood for engaging with people and I was already in a committed relationship. This has nothing to do with that guy. His look of dejection was deep, yet it wasn't his fault that I was unavailable! Always remember that when you are rejected, it is not something to be taken personally. People have to reject most of the time. It is only when two people are in the right time and place together in terms of wanting a relationship, being available for that relationship, and also finding the other person attractive and interesting. Even then, the success of the relationship is not guaranteed. That will be learned through the dating process as time goes on. Much time needs to be spent on dating and building relationships. This is not something that comes quickly or easily, although it usually feels like it does when you meet the right person. Be prepared for life's inevitable rejections.

The best way to prepare yourself for rejection — before even considering dating — is to build up your self-confidence, self-worth, and to fill your life up with things that make you content. A relationship is not meant to save you or heal you from the world. The purpose of a relationship is to enhance an already whole and complete person. You must be happy with yourself, in love with yourself, before someone will fall in love with you. People need other healthy, grounded, well-adjusted people so that the relationship has the best chances of success. We do not want to put the responsibility on another person to have to work to make us happy. It is important to already be content with life, and the person who you're meant to be with will only need to focus on loving you and working with you as a partner in life. This is done by being effective communicators. In order to be good at communicating in your relationship, you must be willing and able to talk about everything, including topics that are difficult to discuss. For example, two people are very much into each other and want to take things to a more sexual level. If you are not comfortable enough with that person to discuss something like birth control, STDs, or sexual history, then you are not yet ready to get physically intimate. It means you need to continue to work on your communication before it is wise to take things to a more sexually physical level. So, how do we communicate effectively? Every conversation involves at least two people. One person speaks and the other actively listens for approximately a paragraph of information. The active listener then recaps what the other person said so that they feel heard and understood, and then the active listener either urges the speaker to continue or becomes the speaker and resumes the interaction. This back and forth continues until one person or the other terminates the interaction. If you can have back and forth conversation in this manner and show each other that you are listening and are genuinely interested in each other's feelings, you are well on your way to a healthy communicative relationship.

After all of that, you are now in a long-term relationship, and it is important to not stop there. You do not simply achieve long-term relationship status and then cease to communicate or work on that relationship. You have to maintain that relationship over a long period of time. The best way to maintain a relationship is to employ trust, reciprocity, and mutual fulfillment —emotionally, physically and sexually. First, trust is being built slowly as you progress to your Level 9 relationship. That trust must continually be nurtured and maintained over and over again. For instance, are you able to rely on each other for important tasks or take care of each other when one is ill? Can you trust your spouse with your feelings, your body, and your future together? That is proven over time through dating, and then is proven time and time again in a long-term relationship or marriage. The same goes for reciprocity. Are you continually practicing reciprocal conversation? Are you able to share and take turns with daily life tasks and responsibilities? If trust and reciprocity are maintained, then it is easy to keep your significant other emotionally satisfied. It also helps to keep your partner physically safe from illness or from carrying too heavy a load. Trust and reciprocity are also the hallmarks of having a healthy and rewarding sex life. Compatibility is most certainly a must when it comes to sex, but being able to trust and communicate and give each other what you need in sexual ways will keep a relationship healthy and content. Finally, when things go wrong in a relationship (and things frequently go wrong), will the two of you work together as partners and teammates to repair the issue, or will you go on autopilot and allow the issue to fester for years until the problem is too big to solve appropriately? If you tackle problems and issues as they come, you are much more likely to maintain your relationship for the long-term. A relationship is an entity that must continually be nurtured in order for it to advance, grow, and succeed.

CHAPTER 8

Achieving Independence

In our society, every child's goal is to one day achieve independence from parental care. Independence means to establish a career and financial stability, successfully undertake daily life tasks, maintain health, manage expenses, maintain financially sustainable employment, live on your own in a residence separate from your parents, become part of a community that allows for interdependence, and have a place and group of people to reach out to and ask for help from when needed.

Let us begin with the subject establishing a career. Whether we begin the journey into adulthood and independence by going to college or university or going straight into a job opportunity, we are taking the first steps towards breaking free from parental oversight and making more and more decisions for ourselves. We have already discussed college/university experiences. We now need to stress the importance of obtaining job experience. When we are in school for the majority of our lives, we tend to learn to master that very specific environment. The job environment is much different from what is experienced at school. As such, obtaining job experience is critical to not only achieving the goal of independence, but to get on the path towards discovering and preparing for your dream job. Now, when I say "dream job," I mean a job you can be good at, that you are passionate about, and that can be developed into a financially sustainable career. Initially, your first job may not be your passion. In the beginning, the actual experience of working is what is most important to open up future possibilities and opportunities. So, the very first step in the right direction towards discovering and obtaining your dream job is to first find a job you are qualified for. You must then work at that job for approximately 1-2 years in order to build up a work history. That work history is an invaluable tool to be used along the path towards your passion.

For instance, a client of mine went to school for animation. Animation is a highly competitive field with few jobs and many qualified applicants. Once this particular client finished his degree, he struggled to find an opportunity to work his dream job as an animator. He had no other related work experience to help get him to where he dreamed to be. When I was able to convince him to look outside the narrow realm of animation positions, he was quickly able to find a job at a college teaching animation. He did not want to do this as his forever job, but working there for approximately 2-3 years gave him the work experience he needed. Also, he used the time to improve upon his animation skills to make him stand out from the other animation applicants. He continued to seek out his dream job, and I am happy to report that he now animates full time at a big animation company. I am beyond proud of his hard work, dedication, and will to never give up. The lesson here is that our dream job or passions do not always automatically get achieved right after school. We must work towards those goals and expect to meet those goals over a period of time when we take steps to improve ourselves and our skills. Once we achieve those goals, we then find that they can change, evolve, and grow into new and exciting things over the course of our careers. Remember, almost any passion can turn into a sustainable career as long as we are realistic about our abilities and understand that a career is not achieved overnight. It forms over time and requires many steps to accomplish and many more steps to maintain over a lifetime.

Those steps are as follows: first graduate high school (or pass your high school equivalency exam) and/or college and enter into the adult world. There may be some transitional steps such as an internship or volunteer work that turns into a job opportunity. However, once schooling is finished, the main objective is to obtain a job that will give you valuable work experience. The goal here is to prove to future employers that you can maintain a job over a period of time without incident. That proof alone will get you far in the job world. I recommend working at a first job for a minimum of 1-2 years before seeking to advance to a more desirable position. Remember, I am describing the step-by-step approach for someone who may be struggling or to prevent struggle to begin with. Some people, though not many, get their dream job right away, while others get a really great job immediately. Most do not. So it is important to build up your job history. That being said, many first jobs are in retail. That may not always be a suitable position for someone on the spectrum, given the fast paced environment and frequent social interaction it requires. For those on the spectrum, I recommend quiet offices or small stores with a more laid back environment to learn and grow. An employer who is patient and understanding is also essential. This is not always easy to find, so spreading the net wide and getting creative with jobs is often necessary. In my experience, there is a job out there for all of us!

Once you have that initial job it, is time to prove yourself. You must be on time, complete your tasks quickly and efficiently, show consistency, work well with the other employees, and follow your supervisor's instructions. It is necessary to be able to do this continuously and build a reputation of reliability and trust. That reputation is what will get you a good recommendation for your next, more desirable position. Sometimes a better position can be found right at your current company and there will be an opportunity to obtain it. Most other times, you have to look elsewhere to find that opportunity. Your second job needs to be something at least related to your field of interest. For instance, if you started in retail but desire to work in accounting, you must seek out a job related to accounting, or one that can lead you to accounting. This is called getting on the path towards your dream job. You then work at your next opportunity for a number of years and either move up in that company or seek out a position on the outside. You continue on your path until you get closer and closer to your passion or your dream job. It sometimes takes many steps to get there with some detours along the way. However, if you stay the course and continue to look for new opportunities and prove yourself each time, you will eventually find employment that is work but is also quite rewarding.

Obtaining a career is probably one of the most difficult and complex tasks needed to achieve independence. Still, there are many more aspects to consider. For example, daily life tasks. In the course of a day, we do countless tasks to keep us functioning effectively. In my case, I wake up in the morning, make my bed, use the bathroom, prepare and eat breakfast, wash the dishes, brush my teeth, throw in some laundry, take a shower, dry my hair, get dressed, and go to work. When I return from work, I change my clothes, prepare dinner, clean up after dinner, finish paperwork or have more sessions, brush my teeth and do my night time routine, unwind and then go back into my made up bed. Those are my daily life tasks on one particular day. Some days I also have to stop at the store or go to a doctor's appointment. Other days I may have a social function or a house project that needs completing. On other days I may have to sit down and pay the bills or schedule a delivery. The point is that these daily life tasks must be mastered in order to truly achieve independence. Since everyone's daily life tasks differ, it is important to make a list with your life coach or someone that knows you well. Together, you will come up with your personal list of daily life tasks that must be completed each day, some days, and those that need to be completed on occasion. Those life tasks must then be integrated into your calendar until you are able to accomplish them on your own with fewer and fewer reminders externally. So, for instance, a daily task for me is making myself breakfast, so that goes on my calendar every day. I only get gas in my car once every week and a half or so. That means I put calendar reminders when I believe I may need to get gas in my car and move it around depending on when I actually need to get it done. Once I am able to independently notice I require gas in my car, and I can just go get it when I have a spare moment, that task is now independently taken care of and I can move on to mastering other important life tasks. I can even remove it from my calendar to make room for new life tasks to master. A solid repertoire of daily life tasks will take you far in your journey towards independence.

Another important aspect of independence is being able to take care of our own health, fitness, and wellbeing. To keep myself healthy, I go to the gym 5 days a week, eat enough calories each day for my body to function adequately, and get regular physicals from my primary doctor. To keep myself happy, I often schedule time to do activities that I enjoy both with myself and with others. Not everyone will have the same exact plan to take care of these needs since everyone has different requirements for survival and happiness, but we all do need to be able to manage health, fitness, and wellbeing in order to achieve independence. So, for instance, a person may walk daily, cook healthy meals 5 days a week, go out to his favorite restaurant on Saturdays, play video games in his spare time, and watch television with the family after dinner on Sundays. That's one possible plan for one person's needs. Creating your own health plan is essential, and then carrying it out on a daily basis indicates independence.

One of the biggest tasks clients hate is, of course, budgeting. In our society, money is necessary for many of life's needs and pleasures. That is the exact reason why budgeting is so important. Money is limited, and we must find a way to plan for everything we first need and then want in order to function independently and not need anyone to bail us out. If your parents are constantly paying your credit cards bills, then you are not functioning independently. You are dependent on someone else's money. The goal is to be as financially self-sufficient as possible. Creating a budget allows you to see how much money you have each month, how much money you will spend on necessities, and how much money you have left over to pay for entertainment and savings. There is a sample budget in the appendix at the end of this book. The reason budgeting can sometimes be so difficult is that the numbers often change from month to month. Our paycheck, grocery bill, utilities, entertainment, and possibly other expenses are never completely consistent. The autistic mind does not like this and it can cause stress when budgeting. I like to overestimate my budget to simplify things and then be pleasantly surprised when there is extra money at the end of the month, so I can splurge and put extra funds into savings. This way, on a tight financial month, the worst case scenario is breaking even.

In order to improve our budget and make budgeting easier over time is to maintain financially sustainable employment. It is one thing to obtain a job by having a strong resumé and nailing a job interview, but it is a completely different thing to keep that job by maintaining work relationships and performing at the expected level in terms of your job duties. Your performance output must stay consistent and grow in order to achieve and maintain a livable salary. This is why we need to find employment we are interested in, have a talent for, and are capable of improving upon our skills over time. The more we advance and get compensated for our abilities and work ethic, the more financially stable we become. This is a very high indicator of a person on their way to achieving total independence. Once we are on our way to becoming financially independent, we can afford housing. Being capable of affording our own place to live is much different from actually living on our own. Living on our own is an amalgamation of all the skills mentioned above. When you are capable of managing your daily life tasks, taking care of your own personal health, successfully budgeting and maintaining your financially sustainable employment, then you are doing a good job in terms of living independently. Things get more complicated, of course, when you begin to add a roommate or a significant other, children, aging parents, simple visitors, and the like. Every individual needs to manage those complications and know their limitations in doing so. My initial goal for each and every client is to get them living as independently as possible, and if we can add more advanced skills to that, we work to make that happen as well.

It is important to understand the word "independence" because we are a society of people, and in reality, we are not truly completely independent. We do rely on others in society to keep our own personal lives running efficiently. For instance, I do not hunt or gather my own food. I go to a grocery store run by and staffed by a group of people who allow me to circumvent a much more time intensive chore. That grocery store doesn't truly work independently as well. It relies on suppliers and farmers and a vast array of other businesses to help keep them running, as well as a customer base that actually buys their products. We are a society of people who work together, and while it is important to do as much as possible for ourselves, we never truly are alone. We are interdependent upon each other. Being interdependent is strikingly different from being dependent. Being dependent means to completely rely on someone else. Being interdependent means working together in a social system designed for all of us to live as independently as possible. Keep this in mind when you find it to be a struggle to succeed at independence. Independence is best achieved when we have a community to work with in order to accomplish our goals.

Most of us live in a town or a city. We belong to organizations such as schools, churches, gyms, community centers, and more. Interdependence that leads to independence is best achieved by developing a relationship with our community and what that community has to offer. For example, a client of mine lives in a township on the main stretch of road that goes through that town. He lives in his condominium independently, and although he cannot drive, he can walk to all of the city establishments to conduct his business. He can go grocery shopping, to the bank, post office, pleasure shopping, experience restaurants, a pool, and other forms of entertainment. He can also access a bus to take him to work in the next township over. He also has relationships with his neighbors and the local townsfolk who keep an eye on him and make him happy during his daily interactions. If he is in trouble, he can reach out to neighbors or local authorities. He can use the telephone or computer to also reach out for assistance. Additionally, he has a job and has developed relationships there which provide additional support. Over the years, he has sought out, developed, and flourished in a community where he is interdependent in order to maintain his independence. Lastly, it is important to note that the most valuable tool you have is your community, and the best way to utilize a community is to remember to ask for help when you need it. The biggest predictor of success in life is not your ability to do everything on your own, but to ask for assistance. That is not weakness — it is something the most successful people in the world are capable of doing and accepting in order to achieve their greatest potential.

PART III: FOR THE PARENTS AND PROFESSIONALS

*Of or working with Adults
on the Autism Spectrum*

FOREWORD

Lori Gassmann, a parent

I remember clearly the day, October 8, 1997. I woke up, just like every morning. In the next second, my heart plummeted, my head whirled, and reality hit. I struggled to grasp the concept — my son is impaired, disabled, somehow different, not the child I had two days before. Yesterday he was diagnosed with Fragile X, a genetic syndrome causing intellectual disability. The future was irrevocably altered, fractured, out of control. It would not be as I imagined. Overcome with grief, I mourned the death of what I had dreamed, what was forever changed. I then struggled with the shock of being the parent of a "child with special needs." On a journey I did not want to travel, having no plan, I pressed forward in researching then second guessing every new therapy or technique, not knowing where to turn. I had given up my career as a Certified Financial Planner (CFP) and wasn't coping well with this unexpected challenge that had been thrown at me. I became consumed with a need to take action.

I read all about child development. Put my child through evaluation after evaluation. The thing the experts all seemed to agree on was the importance of early intervention; they just weren't sure where to start. He was 2 years old and nonverbal. It was determined that he had global apraxia. This is what caused delays in his ability to produce sound and control gross motor movements. The focus then was to get him making sounds and integrate gross motor movement. We began with Speech and Sensory Integration Occupational Therapy. It was not until several years later that I began to realize that while my son had

116

Fragile X, many of his challenges center around not being able to interact with others. Then, I began to focus on therapies and treatments for Autism. Today it is estimated by the U.S. Centers for Disease Control and Prevention, that 50% of males with Fragile X also have Autism.

I researched therapies both mainstream and alternative. In addition to "standard" Speech and Occupational (Sensory Integration) Therapies, the incomplete list is: Auditory Integration Training (AIT), The Listening Program, Electronic Auditory Stimulation (EASe), Holistic Approach to Neuro Development and Learning Efficiency (HANDLE), Picture Exchange Communication (PECS), Sign language, Electroencephalogram Bio Feedback (EEG), Low Energy Neurofeedback System (LENS), Yolk prism glasses with Vision therapy, Interactive Metronome, Thera-suit with Sensory Integration, Hyper Baric Oxygen Therapy (HBOT). Relationship Development Integration (RDI).

We tried dietary and supplement treatments at Pfeiffer Treatment Center, a GFCF diet, Houston Enzymes, and many alternative supplements as well as prescription medications. We have seen Dr. Mel Levin, Dr. Daniel Amen, Dr. Steve Ingersoll, Dr. Randi Hagerman, Dr. Mel Kaplan, Dr. Len Oches to name a few. The list is long. Whether they helped or not, I'll never really know. Sensory integration delays and speech continued to plague him and seemed to further complicate things for him socially.

At the public high school my son attended, he received Special Ed support in mainstream classes. Sounds, lights, eye contact, and certain clothing textures were problematic. Each day he left for school with baseball cap, large, over the ear headphones, and hoodie up. He often sported sunglasses. He was tuned out and not exactly approachable. The echoes in hallways were sufficiently muffled. The hat and hoodie shrouded any unwanted touch and reduced his anxiety. He was safe, but he was isolated.

He spoke in a very fast and high pitch voice, which was hard to follow, often leaving out small but important words like "is, was, that, not." Reading at third grade level in the ninth grade, his vocabulary was somewhat limited, and that affected him both academically and socially. Socially, he was falling farther and farther behind. What turned out to be the saving grace was his fascination with video games, rap and metal music, and adult cartoons such as *The Simpsons*, *Family Guy*, and *South Park*. Not so different from most teen boys.

He was very proficient at video games, and while his handwriting was barely legible, he had no problem working video game remotes! Our family moved across the country and being able to stay connected by playing video games online with the couple of friends he had was a blessing. Playing video games also provided a popular topic for meeting new people. Rap music was another ice-breaker, and if you can follow the words in a rap song, it is probably safe to say you can follow someone talking very fast. It was a way to connect with others even though the contact tended to be one-sided rather than interactive. It was largely a recitation of facts mimicking the cadence and tone of a conversation. In small doses, you didn't really notice.

His desire to learn more about rap and metal music finally provided his need to learn to read. With Wikipedia, he learned the basics of reading while becoming an expert on every detail of rap music. Finally, the adult cartoons. What can I say... they portrayed day-to-day life with humor, sex, drinking, and current events. Not necessarily the format I would have liked, but in retrospect, it worked beautifully.

The looming gap was that interactive, turn taking, reciprocal conversation — it just wasn't there. Neither was much variety in topics he was willing to discuss. It was not so noticeable until you spent some time with him. Every conversation wound up back to either rap music or video games or another of his maybe 5 favorite topics. He wanted to tell you all about different rap songs. In reality, he was just responding to anything you said with a fact he wanted to share. He used multiple phrases from the cartoons, and used them appropriately in context, but it was always those same phrases. Again, there were enough of them that you didn't pick up on it until you had spoken with him a while. Then you saw the repetition. The connection that true reciprocal conversation brings to a relationship was of great concern.

Like most of the discoveries made on this journey, I stumbled across a new resource on the website AutismSpeaks.org — an Autism and Special Needs Life Coach, Jaclyn Hunt. With that, a new door was opened. The gratitude I have for Jaclyn is immeasurable. I never allowed myself to hope for the types of changes and growth my adult son has made. In the last two years, working with Jaclyn weekly via Skype calls, she has developed perhaps the most important relationship of his life. Through her patience and unique understanding of people on the spectrum, she has become a trusted confidant, a guide for thinking about the future, and a true friend. She has accomplished this while maintaining a professional distance while also allowing him enough room to build trust and confidence. Having experienced this level of friendship, he is in position to develop true friendships with others at work, in his community, and in love.

How she did it, I don't know, but now, he actually listens to what you are saying and will have an opinion or question to ask about what you said. He is not just waiting until you finish so he can make a statement on a topic he prefers. He has made huge steps in embracing the fact that he is "on the spectrum," a concept he had previously steadfastly denied. He has advocated for himself at work. He asked his supervisor, who spoke loudly by nature, that they not shout at him, as he found it unsettling.

His speech has slowed, the pitch is normal. No more baseball caps and the headphones are used less often. Hoodies have given way to vests which are covered in patches of Metal Rock Bands. You cannot believe what a conversation starter they are! I have been with him, and one or two people will not only compliment the vest, but will continue to talk for a few minutes about the patches they like. I had no idea how many people from all walks of life love those bands! Enter reciprocal conversation!

For me, this new found, true conversation is the key that unlocks a future for him far beyond those dreams I mourned so many years ago. My hope is that all of the therapies prepared him to flourish. My feeling is that Jaclyn's coaching has benefited him far more than the traditional therapies he had engaged in. As I continue on the journey with him, I do so with greatly diminished apprehension for the one day when the journey is no longer mine to share.

-Lori Gassmann

Footnote: Quote on Centers for Disease Control and Prevention: https://www.spectrumnews.org/news/fragile-x-syndromes-link-autism-explained

CHAPTER 9

The Most Important Things to Know about ASD for Parents

As a life coach who works closely with adults on the spectrum, I am often first contacted by that adult's parents. Most often, this initial contact is from the mother; however, fathers do reach out quite often as well. Other times, I hear from both parents together. The majority of the time, even if two parents are separated or divorced, they are dedicated to doing what's best for their adult child together. On occasion, there are deeper family issues best suited for family therapy, and I make referrals as necessary. In any case, parents are usually the biggest champions for their children and the first people who are equipped to reach out for assistance. Remember, our goal for every client is to get them to a point where they can advocate for themselves, or ask for help when they need it. This does not mean that only parents reach out to me. In fact, I hear from clients directly, from grandparents, siblings, and other professionals all of the time. It's just that parents are the majority of that initial first contact with a potential new client. This is why having a chapter specifically for parents is essential. Quite often, my clients' best friends and main source of social connection and contact are their parents. So, parents are often the key to instigating change and leading the child's team towards progress and success. Eventually, we want the client to become the "team lead," but initially, the parent comes to us in that role. The very first piece of advice I have for parents who are currently the leader of the team and have been for the majority, if not entirely, of that child's life is to mentally prepare to pass that role along to the adult child as we progress towards independence. The reason I say this is because many parents struggle to relinquish this role for a variety of understandable reasons.

For instance, a father once reached out to me about his adult son who is highly intelligent, does well in college academically but needs constant reminders to get up in the morning, get to his appointments, put gas in the car, and more. The father, as a way to help his child cope, has taken on his child's executive functioning duties by waking him up each morning, reminding him of all of his appointments, when to leave to get there on time, and he also keeps the car full of gas whenever he notices it is empty. The father, after having an initial consultation with me, wanted to set up his son's first appointment, while I insisted that we set it up directly with his son. The father was convinced his son would never be able to accomplish that task, and that it would be best done directly through him. Now, sometimes it is very difficult for a client to set up an appointment directly with us; however, the majority of the time it works just fine. We put that client in control and empower him by giving him flexibility and choices in scheduling his own day. We also must work with the parent initially to make sure the adult child is keeping his appointments, because quite often, the consequence is that the parent ends up paying for the missed session. So we work on agreements to give 24 hours notice ahead of time for any cancellations and make clear to the client what the consequence would be for a missed session. Very rarely do we have a client who misses a session, but when they do, they understand the consequence, and we work towards eliminating that behavior over time. We don't want the parent to forever remind their child about the appointment; rather, we want to come up with ways that the adult child can remind himself. Also, it isn't just about remembering for the client, but also to respect the coach's valuable time and respect the parent's generosity in wanting to help his child succeed in life. It can be difficult for a parent to relinquish the role of being the child's executive functioning and essentially being in charge of his child's life. However, despite the difficulty in letting go, we must work through this stage together in order to get that child on the path towards independence and self-sufficiency over time.

Similarly, a parent must have high expectations of his or her child, but we need to make sure those expectations are realistic. I once had a father complain to me that his adult child did not respect him, and he felt his son should show more appreciation and thankfulness for all that he provided over the years. I agree with the father that the child should show appreciation and respect, but what was unrealistic here was that the adult child was trained his entire life to have certain things given to him. His autistic mind couldn't fathom expressing gratefulness for things he was accustomed to getting freely. I myself rarely thank the water company for providing me with water or the electric company for providing me with electricity. The father provided quite well for his son and wanted appreciation that his son did not yet know, learn, or conceptualize how to give. I can teach that over time, of course, but the father failed to understand his son's particular struggles. He simply just demanded it and got angry when his wishes weren't automatically satiated. In this one very particular case based on this one client's individual struggles, the father had unrealistic expectations. For someone who is blind or deaf, the disability is easily seen and recognized. For someone on the spectrum, the disability is much deeper in terms of the social nuances and social comprehension sections of the brain. This particular father saw a highly intelligent son who could function at very advanced levels and assumed he was just being unappreciative on purpose, which was far from the reality. The father could not see the disability. This is often what happens in the world when a highly intelligent client makes social mistakes and the world makes assumptions about that client's ability to function socially because it isn't easy to see the mechanisms that aren't working properly in these situations. So in this example, the father's expectations are high but not realistic. How do we change this expectation to something closer to the client's true level of ability?

First, we identify the client's ability and work to improve that ability over time. Will it ever reach the expectations of the father? Perhaps so, perhaps not, but the father can still learn to recognize the disability and the progress over time. In this case, I begin to work with the client on starting to take on more responsibilities over time. The more the client does for himself, the more he recognizes the amount of work and effort that goes into handling these daily life tasks. We also work on learning other people's perspectives in a variety of situations. When these two separate skills are learned, we then combine them in session to help the client recognize when someone does a favor for us, and also recognizes the level of appreciation that is appropriate for each type and degree of favor or helpful behavior. These steps are broken down into smaller steps for clients that require it and bigger steps for those who can grasp these concepts a little more easily. Over a period of time, the father begins to see progress and receives more and more appreciation for things he had wished for earlier on. The expectation bar rises over time and the father and son are interacting at a healthier level over time. Besides working on the skills, we also need to work on the father's communication. Neurotypicals often stew about things that people should "just know" rather than speaking up and communicating their needs verbally. Most adults on the spectrum need specific verbal instruction in order to understand what is expected of them. For example, as a neurotypical woman, I often expect the door to be held open for me when I enter a building with a male. I also expect the door to be held open if a female enters first out of courtesy, as I would do for both males and females if I entered first. Adults on the spectrum may not pick up on this subtle non-verbal social expectation. Sometimes when I meet a client for the first time, especially in my earlier years of coaching, they would let the door slam in my face. They were not intentionally being rude; rather, they just did not understand and were oblivious to the non-verbal social expectation. For me to get angry at this, knowing my client is on the spectrum, would be ignorant and pointless. Instead, I train both my male and female clients on social conventions expected in society. We communicate and talk about these societal expectations, why they are important, and why it is beneficial to participate in them. So, just as I would communicate with a client when I notice a missed social opportunity, I want parents to communicate in great detail with their children on why these social conventions are necessary and important to learn. Never make assumptions about anyone, and do not be afraid to be blunt and honest with your child. You can still be gentle, but make sure you are explicit and clear about what you are trying to communicate and what you expect. Remember, if you can't break something down into small, step-by-step pieces to explain to your adult child and then expect them to just "know" what to do when you yourself cannot break it down, your expectations are unrealistic. Find someone, like a life coach, to teach you how to break down these expectations and make them achievable for your child.

The majority of parents who come to me for help are so wonderful. They are passionate about helping their children make the most out of this life. Some parents, however, are far too controlling. I had a wonderful client who was making tremendous progress, but he was constantly taking steps back because his parent's would continually take away his freedoms whenever he got closer to independence. They reached out to me to help him become more independent, but each time we got closer to that goal, they would get frightened and put up another obstacle. Whenever we would find him a job that he could get excited about, they wouldn't let him accept the job because it wasn't what they wanted for him. They dictated his social relationships even though we worked hard on making sure he was picking safe, healthy people to surround himself with, and I later found out these parents tracked their son's location on his cell phone. These particular parents also did not allow their son to have a lock on his bedroom door, even after a lengthy discussion with them about why this was the case. According to them, he never did anything wrong, they just wanted to make sure he never had the opportunity to do something wrong by taking away his privacy. This extreme situation hurt me deeply. This adult child had no chances of success when his parents controlled his life so intensely. His potential to be an independently functioning contributing member of society was there, but they would not allow us to get him there. These particular parents did not serve their son's best interests out of their own insecurities and selfishness. They were completely codependent and toxic in terms of their son's growth and progress. This is not the majority of parents out there, but the controlling theme is seen far too often in my line of work.

However, as I said earlier, the majority of parents are wonderful, caring, and very much willing to see their adult child flourish in the world. Some have a hard time stepping back so that their adult child can learn to ask for and receive help from others. Yet, I have had parents say that even though it is hard to let go and let their child design his or her life, it is the best thing for the child. We want parents to be parents again, while we, as coaches, start specifically teaching our clients all the skills needed to function and grow, making sure they also know who to go to for assistance when needed. Sometimes parents get a little confused when we as coaches recommend to the adult child to do something and they go ahead and do it, when the parents have been telling them to do that same task for months or even years. It may just be good for the client to hear it from a new source that isn't as emotionally invested in the situation to push them to comply. Furthermore, I have seen parents do so much for their children, from fighting for their individualized educational plans (or IEPs) to creating social opportunities to starting groups and foundations and more. The dedication and life long commitment these parents have for their children is unlike any other type of love I have seen in the world. I admire and respect the majority of parents out there who are raising children on the spectrum. My one piece of advice in terms of helping your adult children is this: let them do as much for themselves as they are capable of doing, trust them, and make sure we find and develop that independence to the fullest.

Now, with parents that dedicate so much of their lives to their adult children with ASD, it is important to take time to care for yourself and have a separate identity from your child. I once had the pleasure of hearing Dr. Temple Grandin speak at the National Autism Conference in New Orleans, LA, back in September of 2017, and one of the many things that stuck out for me was when she said that one of the greatest things her mother ever did for her was push her out of her comfort zone and make sure that she herself had a life of her own, separate from her child's needs. Dr. Grandin said that by through her mother's independence, she was able to learn to better develop her own sense of independence, separate from her mother, and that was a skill that she took with her for the rest of her life. We are all responsible for ourselves first and our loved ones, friends and the rest of society second, and in that order. I have had many parents tell me that even though life coaching for their adult child is an expense, it is an investment in their future. I believe the same holds true for a parent taking care of their own identity and needs first — it is an investment in yourself that will benefit your child's future. My recommendation for all parents is to make sure you do not dedicate yourself solely to your child, but you should also make sure you have a life outside of the house with a career, hobbies, and socialization. You need to be a whole and complete person in order to best equip your child to be a whole and complete person themselves. This is paramount, and even if it's difficult, you must find ways and utilize every available resource to make sure this happens. I once heard a commencement speaker years ago say, "Put your oxygen mask on first before you attempt to help others." This includes your own family. Do not forget to take care of yourself, and a life coaches can help you navigate that as well.

Lastly, one of the most important things parents need to do that will benefit their adult child well into the future is long-term planning for when they are no longer around. I would say this is the top fear of parents who reach out to me. "What will happen to my adult child when I am gone?" Well, this depends on a great many things. Some clients have more ability than others. You need to first assess your child's current level of functioning and plan accordingly. As time goes on, you can reevaluate your child's level of independent functioning and alter the plan accordingly, but it is always best to start with having as many supports put into place as possible initially — it is much easier to remove supports than to add them later when you are no longer able to or you pass the deadline for doing so. Some clients diagnosed on the spectrum or with other developmental disabilities are entitled to government supports. It is important to put these supports into place as early as possible. You need to apply for social security disability if your child qualifies, and you must fight for it until it gets approved. The best chances a successful approval might include filing multiple times or hiring a lawyer to help you get the language right. Similarly, you should reach out to your local department of developmental disabilities and register for and apply for every service they offer that your child can benefit from. Some services include assistance with independent living, shopping, transportation, social companionship, work supports, house cleaning, and much more. These services need to be put into place as early as possible because it may be extremely difficult for your child to navigate these complex systems on their own. You then need to determine your child's ability to make decisions, both personal and financial, for themselves. A neuropsychological evaluation can be quite beneficial in deeply understanding your child's struggles and what supports would be most helpful. These evaluations can be very expensive, but they are very valuable in terms of what they can tell you about your child and the support he or she requires. If it is determined that your child cannot make big financial or personal decisions on their own, it may be time to appoint guardianship to a trusted relative or friend to assist your child when you are no longer able to fulfill that duty yourself as a parent. Having guardianship established early ensures a smooth transition when you are no longer able to make important decisions for your child. Check with your local county court for more information on guardianship, the duties of a guardian, and how to appoint one. It is best to consult a lawyer for this process to ensure a complete and smooth transition.

Most importantly, financial planning is a way to ensure your child maintains whatever benefits that have been put into place as well as what they inherit from your estate when you are no longer around. It is essential to plan financially, regardless of your level of income or financial status. I recommend consulting with a professional financial planner to address these matters effectively. It is always best to consult with a professional in order to customize and prepare your estate to best serve your adult child when you are no longer able to manage these financial matters on your own. Along with a financial planner, attorney, your adult child's support team, and his or her community network and friendships, you will one day leave this world with a valuable and successful member of society. Your ASD adult child will carry on the family name while taking pride and pleasure in a content and fulfilling life, all thanks to loving and dedicated parents who did their very best — not only to provide for their child, but also gift them with the tools and supports necessary to not only survive but thrive in our very social world.

CHAPTER 10

What Professionals Need to
Understand About Clients with ASD

As I said early on in this book, throughout my graduate training to become a therapist, I only was offered the textbook definition of autism outlined in the Diagnostic and Statistical Manual of Mental Disorders Fourth Edition. There were no classes offered specific to autism or any related conditions. That very clinical definition did not even scratch the surface in terms of how to understand a day in the life of someone with autism, nor did it help to understand a day in the life of the parents, siblings, grandparents, and the professionals that work with these individuals. There are so many difficulties that stem from an autism diagnosis that are not covered in a text devoted to definition and diagnosis. There are textbooks out there on autism, but not every college or university offers that kind of in-depth training in the form of a dedicated course or series of courses. Personally, I feel my training was incomplete, and that's why I took it upon myself to read everything I could on ASD and champion the higher ups in the field to do more research and provide more information on and for adults with autism. Thinking back to when I hired now one of my top coaches, Francesco Paladino, Certified Cognitive Coach, my first training assignment for him was to scour the internet and tell me what kind of information is readily available for and about adults on the ASD spectrum. He was shocked to find that back in 2018, there was very little information available that suited him in the kind of work he was about to undertake as an ASD Life Coach. Throughout the years, I created methods from scratch, and I developed models and systems that would work for the majority of people on the spectrum. I did so because there were no other formal types of training available to professionals like myself. That being said, most therapists do not have formal extensive training in ASD, and these are typically the first source of assistance people on the spectrum seek out to work on their struggles.

There was and still is a great need for this type of formal training, and my advice to professionals of all types who work with this population of people is to strive towards understand autism in adulthood on a much deeper level. Do not be content with the textbook definition or the quick internet search you do in order to understand a client a little better. I recommend finding training, expanding your knowledge, and connecting with colleagues who have more experience to become the most informed and confident professional you can be. You owe that to the client, and you owe it to yourself to be a consummate professional on all levels. Otherwise, if you yourself cannot achieve that level of proficiency, you have to be able to refer out and have a network of professionals who have extensive qualifications to work with someone on the spectrum. I recommend training from IBCCES along with regularly going to conferences dedicated to ASD to obtain your continuing education credits. I myself attend the National Autism Conference in State College, PA, each year to learn the latest research from some of the top professionals in the field. The networking opportunities are invaluable, and I always bring back with me a renewed sense of hope and motivation for my client's futures. There is still much to be discovered about ASD, being that is a very new and evolving condition. Going to these conferences gives us the opportunity to share and collaborate for a more successful future.

Likewise, I believe it is imperative to have a willingness to learn more about the individual you serve rather than just seeing another person, or number, on the spectrum. Each and every one of my clients is different. While I do find a lot of similarities and tackle many problems in a familiar fashion across the board, each client has very unique needs, ways of learning, and ways of responding to me. We must be capable of tailoring each session to the individual. The problem with autism is there is no one size fits all approach to treatment. That is what makes it so difficult to treat autism on a large scale. The key is to become a professional who can be flexible, who can think outside of the box when working with someone on the spectrum. We as neurotypicals have a responsibility to discover the missing pieces for someone who is not even seeing the puzzle. For instance, I was once working with a client who repeatedly failed his written driver's test. He struggled with studying and so desperately wanted to succeed, but the method of studying was terrible for the way he learned. He was no longer in school, so he couldn't take a course to help with learning the driver's manual. I finally suggested he download the hearing impaired soundtrack to the driver's manual, and it completely transformed his studying methods. He was able to absorb the information the way his mind best responded, and he finally passed that driver's test. Another example is when I worked with a client for a number of months and I just couldn't break through to him. He had no desire to do anything with his life. He enjoyed staying in his room playing video games and distancing himself socially from everyone, including his family. Finally, after what seemed like an eternity, I was able to discover that he loved Dungeons and Dragons, a fantasy table top role playing game. Not only did he love the game, he loved creating in-depth and extensive scenarios. We ended up setting him up to do that for a living. and while he isn't getting rich off of his great interest, he's making enough to get by. He now has enough satisfaction with the direction of his life that he is much more willing to take on the other responsibilities he shrugged off in the past. We found something that could give him purpose in life. One last example is of a female client who desperately wanted to find a husband. It took us a long time to get her to see that her goal of getting a husband was too broad and unrealistic. We spent a lot of time talking about what qualities she wanted in a boyfriend that could one day lead to a content and successful marriage. She had never thought of any qualities except that the potential mate would want to marry her. Her goal to be married caused her to lose sight of all the other very important things that constitute a healthy relationship. Three different clients with three very unique struggles. If I went through my list of hundreds of clients, or my coaches lists of thousands of clients, we would see so many varied stories of very unique problems and equally unique solutions. Be the professional who is genuinely interested in learning about each and every client as an individual.

This is a good time to discuss gender differences in ASD. Too often, I have come across professionals who do not recognize ASD in a female or even discount an ASD diagnosis because a male has many friendships. Not every client will exhibit or struggle with all of the symptoms of ASD, and some may actually thrive in the most common areas of struggle for other adults with autism. This does not negate the diagnosis. For instance, females with ASD are much more likely to have friendships and romantic relationships than their male counterparts. The female ASD struggles are often manifested in social misunderstandings, conspiracy theories, and being taken advantage of without recognizing red flags. On the other hand, males with ASD tend to struggle with finding any type of friendship, they tend to desperately crave a romantic relationship, and they are at high risk to make a social mistake that may get them in trouble with the law. These are just some of the possible issues and differences in males and females on the spectrum. Of course, there is overlap, and both genders can struggle with the same exact issues. However, when I see a professional treating ASD males and females the same way, I get frustrated and concerned. We must take each client as an individual and develop a plan of action tailored to their very specific needs. For instance, take a female client who has plenty of friendships and a steady boyfriend who wants to work but fails repeatedly in the retail arena. We focus on helping that client find a job in an environment in which she feels safe and comfortable, while also sharpening her skills to perform that specific job. Another female client may want a boyfriend, but we need to teach her how to recognize red flags so that she does not get her heart broken again by a guy who just used her for rides to work. A male client may desperately want a girlfriend but currently has extremely low self-confidence. Getting a girlfriend isn't going to happen until we build up that self-confidence and self-worth to a point where a girl would find him attractive. Many male clients have such low self-confidence that they conclude that they must be "ugly," when physically, they are actually very attractive. They fail to see that their depression and low self-worth are what's holding them back. When we repair the self-worth, the chances of finding and maintaining a romantic relationship are that much greater. As a professional, you must recognize and take gender and individual differences into account in order to be an effective source of assistance.

In our line of work, clients are often working with more than one professional. Similarly, parents are usually highly involved in their child's life. Highly skilled professionals know that taking a wholistic approach is best. This is because we only see our clients for a limited amount of time each week, while parents and the client spend the most time together. We must maintain confidentiality and trust with a client, but it is very important to keep the lines of communication open with the parents and other professionals that work with our clients. It is important for everyone on that adult child's team to be on the same page. I often work with parents, therapists, case managers, psychiatrists, teachers, and other professionals my clients lean on and value. As a professional, you must strive to be an integral part of this team. You do not work in isolation. This is a client who needs us to be the initial line of a community network that will soon grow to include a work community, a friendship community, and perhaps a romantic relationship that will lead to parenthood and a whole new community of individuals, all part of the client's support system. We are the first line, and we need that line to be strong by uniting together and making sure we cover all of the bases on the client's journey towards independence. Also, by working together effectively, we are demonstrating and modeling to the client how a team works. Clients on the spectrum often struggle with team activities. This is the ultimate team activity when we work to help a client design, live and function effectively in society. You don't just have a commitment to your client, you have a commitment to the entire system that supports that client.

The final recommendation I have for professionals who come across or even work frequently with clients on the spectrum is to make sure that you are willing to recognize your own limitations. I get extremely upset when I hear that a client has been in therapy for 5 years, or even 10 years, without progress. I feel the professional has not recognized their own limitations and has not gone above and beyond to get that client additional support. It is not therapeutic to be in therapy for that length of time. My coaching is designed to see clients for approximately 6 months, where we start off with weekly sessions to delve into the theory of all the skills we teach. Once we get into practicing those skills over a period of time, we back off and allow the client space to succeed more and more on his or her own. Soon we are seeing the client on a monthly basis, and then on an as needed basis — of course, with the understanding that we are always there for a maintenance session or series of sessions depending on what we are working to accomplish. There are clients that are seen on a much longer basis, but the ultimate goal is to get them relying on us less and less over time. To allow a client to become dependent on us is not a service. The goal must always be to get them as independently functioning as possible, to the point where we as professionals are utilized as a support when help is needed, and we take a step back to let the client shine when they are capable of handling things on their own. If this is not happening over time, it is the professional's responsibility to recognize his or her own limitations and try something different by referring out, adding another professional, and discussing your concerns with the client. Our top priority is the client, always.

CONCLUSION

The Importance of Life Coaching for Adults on the ASD Spectrum

A while back, I wrote an article on the importance of life coaching for adults on the autism spectrum. You can do an internet search and easily find it. I was a bit more green back then and still had a lot to learn. In fact, I am continually learning and growing as a professional. The book you read today will be completely transformed 10 years from now as we learn more about ASD and as the ASD population rises. We will learn how to better work with those on the spectrum, and many of my methods will evolve and become more effective over time. Similarly, new and more advanced methods will arise. Also, it is important to note that through my work, my clients have had a tremendous effect on my personal life. They have taught me to be more honest, straightforward, blunt (to the distress of some neurotypicals), patient, understanding, and motivated in my own life. They teach me so much about their interests, hobbies, and passions that I would most likely never have had the opportunity to learn about otherwise. They enrich my life more than I ever thought possible. Because of my clients and the experiences I have had with them over the years, I feel the true importance of life coaching is to help my clients share these rich, meaningful aspects of themselves — not just with me but with the rest of the world. I want to take these isolated treasures of people and share them with everyone else. In my work, I have had the privilege of knowing and becoming friends with some of the most loving, kind, passionate, intelligent, and interesting people in the world. We need to coach them so that the rest of the world can benefit from their richness and their love. I could not imagine my life without being influenced and impacted by each and every one of my clients. I do not want to imagine a world without their tremendous positive influence.

Another reason life coaching is important for adults on the spectrum is because quite often, we are told by society what to do with our lives. A life coach's job is to help the client design his or her own life, not the life others want for them. For example, I had two parents tell me they wanted their son to have a girlfriend. I get that request quite often. However, after getting to know the son over the course of a few sessions, I quickly learned that he had no interest in a romantic relationship of any kind. In fact, his parents continually pushed it on him because they didn't want him to be sad and alone. The reality was that the only thing making this client feel sad was the constant pressure put on him by his parents to find a girlfriend. And in terms of loneliness, he had one or two people that satisfied his social needs, and he was actually not lonely at all. Once I learned this, I was able to assure him that a girlfriend is not something he should seek out unless he desired it. My job as a life coach is not to tell you what you need or want. I am working for the client and helping them to achieve what they desire, or if they do not know what they desire, my job is to help them figure it out. Once he knew he did not have to comply with his parents wishes, he was quite relieved. Consequently, I had to have quite a few discussions with the parents, and luckily, I was able to convince them that their son was still whole and complete all by himself. They eventually backed off. Today, that client is living independently in his own apartment and content with his life. He is relieved he does not have to take care of anyone but himself. That is not selfish, that is an intelligent person knowing what he wants and designing his life accordingly. Life coaches are here to help you design your life in your vision. Just like an athlete or musician needs a coach or trainer to reach his or her fullest potential, many of us need a life coach to achieve the very same thing.

So where do you find help? Reading this book was a great start! You sought out information. Many will find this book useful as a guide to coach themselves. Others may need a little more hands on training. My team of coaches and I are here and taking on new clients all over the United States. You can learn more about what we do at www.asdlifecoaches.com. It is important to note that this book is not intended to solely promote my company. I am very passionate about changing the way autism is treated here in the United States. In this country, we treat autism as a medical condition or a mental illness. The fact is that ASD is a social and communicative disorder that does not only require therapy and medication, it requires intense social and communication training. It is my great hope that the leaders in the field of autism research will recognize and do more research on the effectiveness of social training in the ASD population. Additionally, I implore insurance companies and disability services across the country to recognize not just my services but all similar services across the globe. The purpose of this book is to raise awareness about the side of autism not easily seen by simply looking at a person from the outside. We can't have autism awareness without understanding. I want this book to help the layman understand what autism truly is, and how they can help recognize and nurture those who are struggling socially rather that shunning and contributing to their isolation. So to find help, utilize your local department of developmental disabilities, research ASD on the internet from reputable sources, reach out to me and my team of coaches. If we cannot help, we will certainly do our best to point you in the right direction, and most of all, be a helper yourself. When you see someone anxious or processing slowly, give them time and encouragement to respond. If you notice someone is lonely, give them a few minutes of your time. Make this world a more accepting and understanding place so that it doesn't have to be as scary and intimidating as so many of my clients find it to be. Lastly, I myself made a very conscious decision in my life to do my very best to never be the person to brush someone off and be the trigger for them to give up on life. There were so many times in my own past where I wish someone would have recognized my pain. I was lucky to have had people who were kind enough to lead me to a much better place. If we can help guide just one person out of darkness, we have accomplished a great service to the human race.

The future of understanding and treating ASD, particularly in adulthood, has a very bright future. Children are being identified much earlier in life, and early intervention has been one of the best ways to catch these kids up to their peers in terms of social and emotional functioning. Still, there are many who are currently in adulthood or are entering adulthood who did not get enough life preparation. That is changing and life coaching is only just the start of this change. If you look at the statistics, we are becoming a more autistic world. We are going to be forced to adapt to this great change in how we communicate as a society. Social media has contributed to both a worldwide information overload as well as a major social disconnect. Loneliness is rising as we become more electronically attached. I believe that reconnecting with nature, the simple things in life, and disconnecting from the collective will be what the future holds if we want to maintain and develop our humanity to its fullest potential. To all the ASD adults in the world: I need for you to never give up, to continue to try your best, even if your best varies from day-to-day, and above all else, I need you to set aside your doubts and inhibitions and simply remember to accept your greatness.

AFTERWORD

Joseph Hunt, Husband, CEO
of his own company

For my Love,

I am very proud of you for completing your first book. Congratulations! Many people say that they will write a book one day but only very few are able to follow through, finish it and publish it. I think that you did an excellent job of showing the autism spectrum from the perspective of the affected person, the parents and from the life coaching viewpoint as well, while tying everything together. I think it is a must read for anyone who is on the spectrum, knows someone who is or who wants to learn more about autism.

Over the years, I watched how Jackie developed her techniques using her experiences working with many different people on all ends of the spectrum and witnessed how she has helped countless people improve their lives. In the past, when I was researching available information on adults with autism, there was not a lot of useful information to be found and nothing that matched with what Jackie was having success with when coaching her clients. I think the importance of this book is that it is a different perspective than the existing available information and has a lot of new material that hasn't been formally documented before. The definition of high functioning autism in the American Psychiatric DSM book is not very detailed and includes one size fits all treatments instead of recognizing that every individual case is completely different. Many therapists today lack the tools and training to help adults on the spectrum. This book will help change that.

When my wife asked me to write the afterword for her book to tie everything together, I was having a hard time figuring out what to write because I don't choose to identify with being on the autism spectrum. She told me that I just needed to write what I think. I can relate and understand from everyone's perspective both neurotypicals and people on the spectrum. Jackie says I am neurodivergent, or that I think differently from the majority of people in the world. It is my understanding that many people on the spectrum have a social learning disability. They have a hard time communicating with others and also seeing other people's perspectives. Like other learning disabilities- extra help, repetition, practice, tutors and other support will lead to improvement. Many children do not get all of the help that they need or become reliant on the help that is available and when they turn into adults, suddenly they need to handle everything on their own and services are much more limited or non-existent. This is where coaching comes in. Life coaches specializing in helping people on the autism spectrum can help give guidance and direction to an individual new to adulthood who is having trouble navigating the social aspects and novel responsibilities of adulthood.

Personally, I have spent a lot of time over the years identifying and eliminating any traits that I had that would have put me on the spectrum as a child and evolved socially over time. I believe that continuous improvement and communication apply to all situations neurotypicals and spectrum individuals face alike. Over the years, I have improved communication within my business and in my personal life, relationships and with family. Many of the techniques described and explanations of how different people think can be used to improve communication for both ASD and neurotypicals. This works for everyone.

Just some background on myself; I started my own company back in 2012. Building a business from scratch and creating something from nothing was one of the most rewarding things that I could have done in my life. Instead of following the norm and working to make someone else's vision come true, I was able to create my own company, with the help of some great coworkers, and was able to grow bigger than the previous company that I had worked for over the years. When building my company, I didn't rely on books or following the norms but relied on common sense and experience to create anew my own methods to build something from nothing. The same can be said for this book as Jackie derived from her experiences a new way of dealing with an existing problem and extracted her own unique solutions. Creativity of this kind doesn't exist much in a society where everything can be looked up in a search engine and whatever comes out on the top page is what is followed. Since there wasn't a developed career path in this field she created her own...and now she has many coaches expanding exponentially how many people they can help.

To wrap things up, the goal of this book is to help as many people as possible and hopefully inspire new life coaches and changes in existing treatments. By reading all sections whether you are on the spectrum, a parent of someone on the spectrum, someone who works with or helps anyone on the spectrum or someone who just wants to learn about autism in general will greatly increase your knowledge and understanding of ASD. Lastly, anyone can do anything they work hard at as long as they set their mind to it. Sometimes it's hard to put together a plan or know where to start. For anyone on the spectrum who wants to improve, this book is a good place to start. Remember, one of the most important success criteria in life is being happy. People can be different and be happy. If you are not happy then you need to do something different and try to find new ways to fix whatever is keeping you from happiness. Anyone who is on the spectrum, or anyone in general, can achieve this. You can make your own happiness. If you are happy in life, then you are a success.

BIBLIOGRAPHY

American Psychiatric Association (2013). *Diagnostic and Statistical Manual of Mental Disorders 5th Edition.* Washington, DC: American Psychiatric Publishing.

Grandin, T. (2015). *The Way I See it: A personal look at Autism & Asperger's Fourth Edition.* Arlington, Texas: Future Horizon's Publishing.

Perry, Y. (2010). *Whose stuff is this? Finding freedom from the thoughts, feelings and energy of those around you.* St. Francis Bay, South Africa: Write On! Publishing.

Rath, T. (2007). *Strengths Finder 2.0.* New York, NY: Gallup Press.

Ruiz, d. M. (2018). *The Four Agreements: A Practical Guide to Personal Freedom.* Amber-Allen Publishing, Incorporated.

Volkmar, F., Paul, R., Rogers, S.J., Pelphrey, K.A. (2014). *Handbook of Autism and pervasive developmental disorders , assessments, interventions, and policy.* Hoboken, NJ: Wiley.

WEBSITES

Autism and Special Needs Life Coach LLC
www.asnlifecoach.com

ASD Life Coaches LLC
www.asdlifecoaches.com

International Board of Credentialing and Continuing Education
Standards
www.ibcces.org
Use code ASD20 for 20% off certification

James V. Carroll - Cover Artist
www.jvcarroll.com

Interest Profiler
www.mynextmove.org

Meetup
www.meetup.com

Journal of Autism and Developmental Disorders
https://www.springer.com/journal/10803

Check out Love on the Spectrum on Netflix

APPENDICES:

SAMPLE COVER LETTER

Jaclyn Hunt
Colonia, NJ 07067
732-675-6876
asnlifecoach@gmail.com

February 1, 2021

Joseph Hunt
CEO
All the Rages Inc.
355 Eisenhower Parkway Suite 101
Livingston, NJ 07039
973-551-1277

Dear Mr. Joseph Hunt:

The reason for this letter is to inquire about the Human Resource position at your company. I learned of this opening by browsing the job listings on your website www.alltherages.com. I am interested in applying for this position.

I have an interest to be in human resources because I enjoy working with people and helping to see them through to their fullest potential. I believe my cognitive coaching experience, as outlined on my resume, would be highly beneficial in terms of being successful in this position. I have a passion not only to see each individual succeed at your company but to also see the company thrive as a whole.

Enclosed find my resume. It outlines my skills and experience as it relates to this position. At your earliest convenience, I would like to meet with you to discuss the possibility of working as your human resource department for your company. I can make myself available at your earliest convenience as long as it does not interfere with my current client schedule. You can contact me at the number or email listed above. I intend to follow up with you in one week's time. Thank you very much for considering my application. I look forward to hearing back from you.

Sincerely,

Jaclyn Hunt
Enclosure - Resume

SAMPLE RESUME

JACLYN HUNT
Colonia, NJ 07067
Phone: 732-675-6876
Email: asdlifecoaches@gmail.com

OBJECTIVE

To provide cognitive coaching services for adults on the autism spectrum, spouses and significant others of adults on the autism spectrum, parents of children and adults on the autism spectrum, educators, doctors, case managers and other professionals that work with those on the autism spectrum, as well as all those affected by Autism Spectrum Disorders.

EDUCATION

January 2005 – May 2006 Kean University, Union, NJ
   M.A. (Master of Arts) – Behavioral Sciences with a Specialization in Psychological Services
   GPA 3.76/4.0
September 2000 – May 2004 Rutgers University, New Brunswick, NJ
   B.A. (Bachelor of Arts) – Psychology
   GPA 3.0/4.0

EXPERIENCE

ASD Life Coaches LLC – 2018 - PRESENT
Owner
Manages a team of seven cognitive coaches
Provides consultations to potential clients before assigning a suitable coach
Utilizes various forms of social media and old fashioned advertising methods
Designs classes and workshops aimed at educating ASD Adults, parents and professionals

Autism and Special Needs Life Coach LLC – 2013 - PRESENT
Life Coach and Managing Member
Teaches adults on the autism spectrum various real-life skills
Provides emotional support and instruction to spouses of adults on the autism spectrum
Advises, guides, and assists parents of children on the autism spectrum
Conducts classes for parents, couples, and families affected by ASDs
Works with professionals dealing with adults on the autism spectrum
Speaks and conducts workshops to bring awareness and methods of action to community organizations dealing with people on the autism spectrum and their families

Metro Glass Inc, New Brunswick, NJ – 2000-2013
Duties included:
Communicated with company contacts verbally and in writing
Assisted human resource department by providing guidance and direction to company employees
Gathered. analyzed, and organized data for departmental use
Summarized information to various department heads
Engaged in various administrative duties
Created proposals for potential clients using MS Office

Psychology Research Laboratory, Rutgers University – Summer

2003
Duties included:
Interviewed students and teachers in various schools and settings
Supervised and participated in data collection, data entering, data clean-up, and coding of data
Filed, organized computer files and hardcopy files, organized laboratory space
Analyzed and prepared material to be used in the research of various laboratory members for future academic publication

PUBLISHED WORKS

Hunt, J (2014 September). Highlights from the August Autism Conference Autism Parenting Magazine Issue 23, 22-26.

Hunt, J (2014 June). Motivation Autism Parenting Magazine Issue 19, 21-23.

Hunt, J (2014 February). Q & A. Autism Parenting Magazine Issue 15, 26-29.

Hunt, J (2014 January). Death, Grief, and Autism. Autism Parenting Magazine Issue 14, 40-42.

Hunt, J (2013 December). Let go of Your Expectations this Holiday Season. Autism Parenting Magazine Issue 13, 33-36.

Hunt, J. (2013 October). Don't Desensitize...Recognize!. Autism Parenting Magazine Issue 11, 21-23.

Hunt, J. (2013 August 26). The Transition from High School to College...while on the Spectrum. Autism Parenting Magazine Issue 10, 28-30.

AFFILIATIONS

Advanced Certified Autism Specialist Level 2
IBCCES, International Board of Credentialing and Continuing Education Standards, License ACAS173346
December 2017 - Present

Board Certified Cognitive Specialist
IBCCES, International Board of Credentialing and Continuing Education Standards, License BCCS176402
March 2017 - Present

Certified Autism Specialist
IBCCES, International Board of Credentialing and Continuing Education Standards, License CAS134999
December 2013 – December 2017

Nationally recognized for academic excellence in psychology as a member of PSI CHI: The National Honor Society of Psychology
Excellent personal and professional references available upon request

SAMPLE MONTHLY BUDGET

Sample Monthly Budget Items

Mortgage/Rent:
Homeowner's or Renter's Insurance:
Maintenance:

Food:
Toiletries and/or Living Necessities:

Bills
    Gas:
    Electric:
    Sewer/Water:

Transportation
    Car
        Gas:
        Maintenance:
    Insurance:

    Public Transportation:
    Taxi or other pay Transport:

Savings:

Other Expenses likely but NOT mandatory
    Cell phone:

Internet:
Cable:
Entertainment:
Luxury Items:

Compare above totals to your total monthly income:

TIME MANAGEMENT
JOURNAL

Wake up Routine: Examples are making and having breakfast, showering, getting dressed, preparing to go to work, etc.
   Time needed:

Morning Routine: Examples are commuting to work, getting your coffee, walking the dog, feeding the cat, doing morning chores, etc.
   Time needed:

Midday Routine: Examples are having lunch, making phone calls, tidying up, etc.
   Time needed:

Afternoon Routine: Examples are Finish up day's work, check the traffic report, freshen up, etc.
   Time needed:

End of Day Routine: Examples are commute home, stop for gas, run to the store, plan dinner, etc.
   Time needed:

Evening Routine: Examples are prepare dinner, have dinner, change out of work clothes, check internet or read emails, etc.
   Time needed:

Go to Bed Routine: Examples are watch tv, play video games, read, get changed, brush teeth, prepare for the morning, etc.

Time needed:

SAMPLE DAILY LIFE PLAN

These are only examples of possibilities. Every individual's Daily Life Plan is unique.

Daily Morning Life Tasks:
-Wake self up
-Prepare and have breakfast
-Brush teeth
-Shower
-Get dressed
-Catch bus to work

Daily Afternoon Life Tasks:
-Purchase and have lunch
-Check self hygiene (odors, teeth, grooming, clothing)
-Finish up work for the day
-Catch bus back home

Daily Evening Life Tasks:
-Tidy up house
-Start dinner and clean up dinner
-Prepare for next morning
-Go to bed on time

Weekly Life Tasks:
-Buy weekly bus ticket
-Do laundry
-Check in with parents
-Go through the mail

-Grocery shopping

Monthly Life Tasks:
-Pay the bills
-Clean the living space
-Shop for living essentials

Yearly Life Tasks:
-Make and go on doctor's appointments
-House maintenance

FRIENDSHIP PYRAMID

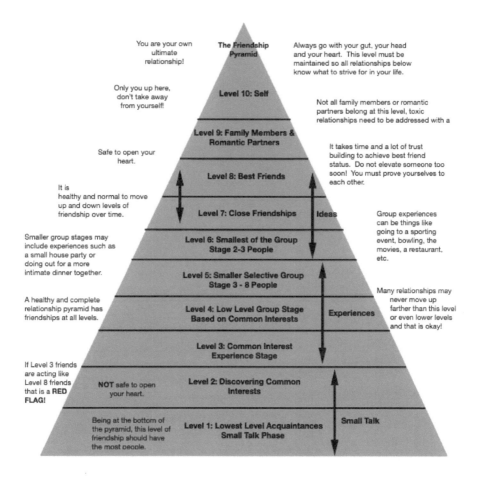

You are your own ultimate relationship!

The Friendship Pyramid

Always go with your gut, your head and your heart. This level must be maintained so all relationships below know what to strive for in your life.

Only you up here, don't take away from yourself!

Level 10: Self

Not all family members or romantic partners belong at this level, toxic relationships need to be addressed with a

Level 9: Family Members & Romantic Partners

Safe to open your heart.

It takes time and a lot of trust building to achieve best friend status. Do not elevate someone too soon! You must prove yourselves to each other.

Level 8: Best Friends

It is healthy and normal to move up and down levels of friendship over time.

Level 7: Close Friendships

Ideas

Group experiences can be things like going to a sporting event, bowling, the movies, a restaurant, etc.

Smaller group stages may include experiences such as a small house party or doing out for a more intimate dinner together.

Level 6: Smallest of the Group Stage 2-3 People

Level 5: Smaller Selective Group Stage 3 - 8 People

A healthy and complete relationship pyramid has friendships at all levels.

Level 4: Low Level Group Stage Based on Common Interests

Experiences

Many relationships may never move up farther than this level or even lower levels and that is okay!

Level 3: Common Interest Experience Stage

If Level 3 friends are acting like Level 8 friends that is a **RED FLAG!**

NOT safe to open your heart.

Level 2: Discovering Common Interests

Being at the bottom of the pyramid, this level of friendship should have the most people.

Level 1: Lowest Level Acquaintances Small Talk Phase

Small Talk

ABOUT THE AUTHOR

Jaclyn Hunt

Jaclyn Hunt MA, ACAS, BCCS holds a Master's Degree in the Behavioral Sciences with a Specialization in Psychological Services from Kean University in Union, NJ. Additionally, she is an Advanced Certified Autism Specialist Level 2 and Board Certified Cognitive Specialist from the International Board of Credentialing and Continuing Education Standards (IBCCES.org). She serves primarily as a Life Coach for Adults on the Autism Spectrum both in-person in her home state of New Jersey as well as all over the world via video conferencing software.

Throughout her career, Jaclyn has worked with hundreds of adults, teaching various real-life skills that most people in the world learn more intuitively than others. She strongly believes that everyone she works with has the potential to progress and grow beyond their present level of functioning. This belief is not only held for her clients who happen to be on the ASD Spectrum but also held and practiced in her daily life.

Jaclyn loves meeting new clients and maintaining a steady client base where she gets the opportunity to share experiences and be part of the lives of people all over the world. She also manages a team of coaches trained specifically to work with Adults on the Autism Spectrum while adding their own unique personalities and techniques to her own tried and true methods of real-life skills training. Her hobbies include working out, reading, occasionally playing video games, taking tropical vacations with her husband Joseph, tasting foods and wines from around the world and, of course, enjoying life to the fullest.

Made in United States
Troutdale, OR
05/28/2023

10297106R00098